WOLVERINE
Creates the World

WOLVERINE
CREATES THE WORLD
LABRADOR INDIAN TALES

Collected and Retold by
LAWRENCE MILLMAN

CAPRA PRESS
SANTA BARBARA

Illustrations by Judy Sutcliffe.
Typography by Pagination Station.

Some of these stories have appeared in: *Boston Globe Magazine,
Northeast Indian Quarterly, Mid-American Review, Shaman's Drum,
The Pantheon Book of Northern Tales, The Northern Raven,
The North American Review, Coming to Light, Elements*
and *Noh Quarter.*

Library of Congress Cataloging-in-Publications Data

Millman, Lawrence.
Wolverine creates the world : Labrador Indian tales / Lawrence
Millman.
p.   cm.
Includes bibliographical references (p. 152).
ISBN 0-88496-363-2 : $12.95
1. Montagnais Indians—Legends. 2. Naskapi Indians—Legends.
I. Title.
E99.M87M55   1993
398.2′089′973—dc20   92-46340
                                      CIP

CAPRA ☙ PRESS
P.O. Box 2068, Santa Barbara, CA 93120

ACKNOWLEDGMENTS

After a fashion, this is a book of debts. I couldn't have traveled around nether Labrador were it not for the good services of Lab Airways (W. C. Pike) and Air Nova (Mary Keith). Nor could I have met my expenses during these travels except for the kindness of the Newfoundland-Labrador Department of Development (Kay Coxworthy). But my greatest debt is to those Innu, some living, others passed on to the eternal *mukoshan,* who gave me the gift of their stories: Uinipapeu Rich, Gilbert Rich, Philip Rich, Tshinish Pasteen, Thomas Pastitshi, John Poker, Gabriel Noah, Apinam Ashini, Hank Penashue, Philip Michel, John Michel, Mary Michel, Matthew Rich, and Luke Nui. *Tshinaskumitin!*

Lawrence Millman
Cambridge, Massachusetts
January 1992

TABLE OF CONTENTS

Introduction: The Dream People

Night falls on Utshimassits, Labrador. Outside the tent, it's cold. Inside the tent, it's cold, too. Somewhere a dog or a wolf is howling, hard to say which. Or perhaps it's the wind howling down from the height of land. Two grizzled crones take turns spitting into an empty lard bucket. Then my host, a tubercular wraith of a man named Thomas Pastitshi, spits into this selfsame bucket and begins telling a story about the time Wolverine, trickster hero of the Labrador Indians, got stuck inside a bear's skull. His laughter, albeit accompanied by a bad cough, transforms the family tent into a voluptuous palace ...

I daresay Labrador is off most peoples' map. No one seems to know where it is, apart from the fact that it presumably lies up there in the vast and inhospitable North. Even the Canadian postal service doesn't know where it is: Labrador's mail routinely ends up in El Salvador. Subarctic barrens, glacial erratics, and mosquito-infested muskeg would appear to have precious little human accessibility—certainly less accessibility than El Salvador or indeed the Amazonian rain forest, another remote locale that's become quite user-friendly of late.

As for the Labrador Indians, they're off the map, too.

Who or what they are, or where they came from, is anybody's guess. Maybe they're a splinter band of Eastern Cree separated from the main group way back in Native American dream time. Or maybe they were dwellers of the deciduous woodlands driven north by the fierce Iroquois. Or maybe, just maybe, they're the last tatterdemalion remnant of a band of Ice Age hunters now wholly lost to history. Yet whatever their origin, they are among the least known, least assimilated, and least anthropologized Natives in North America.

Sometimes called Naskapi or Montagnais-Naskapi, though not by each other (Naskapi means "crude ones" in their language), nowadays Labrador's Indians call themselves Innu, a name which means "The People." It's a happily egocentric name which seems to consign everyone else to another species. It's also a name that invariably gets the Innu confused with their time-honored enemies, the Inuit. But whereas most of the Labrador Inuit inhabit one large town, Nain, the Innu live in two scruffy little villages, Utshimassits and Sheshashui, more than two hundred miles apart. And whereas the Inuit are now mostly employed as commercial fishermen, the Innu—at least the older, more entrenched Innu—still cling to a traditional hunter-gatherer lifestyle. Many of them camp out in the bush, trapping and hunting caribou, from October until late March. That's a time of year when Labrador's temperatures commonly drop to fifty or sixty degrees below zero and the snow tends to pile up in Biblical proportions. The People seem to like such weather.

I first visited Utshimassits, otherwise known as Davis Inlet, in early September 1986. Before I went, a friend warned me to watch out for rocks. The previous year he'd tried to land there in his sea kayak and was repelled by rock-throwing teenagers. Rather than risk injury to his craft or his person, he'd made his landfall farther up the coast, in Shango Bay.

This story piqued my curiosity, maybe even my masochism (all writers are masochists by nature), so the very next day I hopped the mail flight from Goose Bay to Utshimassits. The trip was a story in itself, beginning with the NATO-F4 Phantom that nearly clipped us upon takeoff. Our plane got as far as Makkovik, kicked and buffeted by the boreal elements, and then seemed to break down. Actually, it ran out of fuel. The only fuel in Makkovik was helicopter fuel, for which a filter was needed. And as there was no filter in Makkovik, a special plane had to fly one in from Goose Bay. Bad weather in Goose Bay, filter delayed. Then when the plane did arrive, suddenly Makkovik's generator conked out. No power, no fuel. The pilot wandered off into the tundra to pick berries.

Ah, Labrador, I thought: where nothing is easy. Just as I'd resigned myself to spending the next day or two in Makkovik, the generator sputtered back to life. In another half hour, we were again airborne ... and flying into something that resembled bechamel sauce. It was a major storm. Sleet, snow, and ice pellets quickly rendered the windshield wipers useless and the front window opaque. The pilot, undaunted, kept rolling down the side window and sticking out his head to see where we were going. Each time he did this, the Innu gentleman sleeping next to me would jerk awake and snarl what I assumed was the Inueimun version of *Shut the window, motherfucker* ... Later, when I got to know a little of the language, I realized he couldn't have said that, for Inueimun has no approximation of "motherfucker." Probably the fellow had just been saying: *It's freezing in here!* A not unusual Labrador sentiment.

At last the plane touched down in Utshimassits. It was almost with relief that I braced myself for a pelting of rocks. The rocks never came. Too bad. I'd been hoping for perhaps a chunk or two of four-billion-year-old komatiite, the world's oldest rock and a rarity found only in northern Labrador.

Instead of stoning me, The People kept walking over and shaking my hand gratuitously. They seemed to regard me, a White Person, as a unique specimen of humanity. Doubtless that's because not too many of my race make it to this farflung Native fastness. Those who do are either social workers or government representatives. I suspect my kayaking friend had been mistaken for one of the latter, which would explain the geologic missiles.

Within minutes of my arrival, a man with a cuprous, epicanthic face invited me into his tent, a tent which he rightly preferred to his uninsulated tract house next door. After he'd given me a cup of tea, he took out a bear patella and put it on top of the stove: if the patella moved, he said, today's hunt would be a success; if it didn't, well, it was back to bed. Meanwhile the man's wife was cleaning out their kids' noses the traditional way: by sucking out the mucal matter and spitting it on the floor.

I thought this a rather good introduction to the Innu. Yet by far the best introduction to a new culture comes from camping on the land where that culture itself is encamped. So it was that I left this man (he was going to bed anyway) and trekked off into the bush. Or, as it's referred to in these parts, "the country." Four or five miles north of Utshimassits, I stopped and pitched my own tent. The next few days I cultivated my solitude. Made bannock. Fought off insects. Studied my English-Innu dictionary. Made more bannock. Fought off more insects. And gazed up at a sky so clear, so unpolluted, so starkly blue that I felt I could reach up and touch it had I a mind to do so.

One thing I noticed during those few days: there was almost no wildlife. Apart from the acupuncturing black flies and mosquitoes, I saw only a couple of partridges and one lemming. Fortunately I didn't have to live off the land or I would have been very hungry, a plight which (alas!) would have enhanced my understanding of The People. For the desperate hustle for game is, or was, the driving force behind their existence. So sparse was this game that they'd often try to "dream" it; for instance, a dream of claw marks on a tree would indicate a hibernating bear inside a nearby tree. Or they'd try to divine it—the char on a burnt scapula bone would tell them the whereabouts of a particularly recalcitrant herd of caribou. If all else failed, there was always a certain unmentionable cuisine. Around 1900 the Hudson Bay trader Sebastien Mackenzie found an Innu woman who was pounding up the bones of her family for soup (she'd already consumed their flesh and entrails). That this woman had violated the deepest of human taboos is a tribute to her utter dereliction, along with the dereliction of the land.

Another thing I couldn't help but notice: this derelict land itself. It seemed to grow primarily moss and boulders. If you rotated the crops, you'd get boulders and moss. In more or less verdant areas, there'd be the occasional black spruce, a tree seemingly twisted by some complex inner torture. Such flora helps explain why The People never labored under the delusion, so dear to their Native brethren, that the Earth was their mother. For them, our planet was a lowdown, niggling place, conspicuously lacking in maternal teats. Just to survive on it stretched all their resources. Small wonder that they turned the wolverine—that largest, most canny, most predacious member of the weasel family—into a sort of culture hero. The wolverine is the North's ultimate survivor.

I was not a survivor myself. After four days in the country, I retreated to Utshimassits. There something quite miraculous occurred: it was as if I'd been studying German irregular verbs and suddenly one of them burst into flames.

I'd located a bilingual man, Uinipapeu Rich, to help me with an elder who spoke no English. Back in 1933, this elder, Tshinish Pasteen, found a set of bones that may or may not have belonged to Jim Martin, guide of the ill-fated Koehler Expedition. I was curious about this expedition, so I inquired about the bones. Uinipapeu translated. Tshinish shrugged. Whose bones they were he had no idea. A small White Man's. A large White Man's. He couldn't be sure. More or less as a consolation prize, he told me a story ("How the Birds of Summer Were Brought North") about a little boy who wasn't really a little boy at all.

"You are interested in old stories?" Uinipapeu asked later. And he told me a story about a woolly mammoth ("The Birth of Tchakapesh") which not only fetched me back to the early Pleistocene, but also suggested that this animal, extinct elsewhere in the world, was an active if not a downright malevolent force in Utshimassits.

LM: "That's kind of scary. A mammoth stomping people and then eating them."

UR: "Not as scary as the time I got trapped in a revolving door in St. John's, Newfoundland. *That* was scary, man. I'd rather take my chances with the mammoth ..."

I decided to take my chances with the mammoth, too.

So I started going to Uinipapeu's house for stories. Here, I thought, is the long-lost history of the Innu; a history made up of giants, monsters, and talking animals rather than mundanities like kings and World Wars.

One day Uinipapeu told me one of his father's favorite stories, "The Shit Man," as a Hulk Hogan video was playing in the background. While Hulk was making mincemeat of a fellow wrestler more paunch than man, Uinipapeu's brood of kids looked on in silent wonder. No doubt they were admiring all that resplendent flesh: a thin physique, in their culture, is associated with starvation.

Ideally, Hulk Hogan is not the best context for Innu storytelling. The best context is the so-called country. On a winter's night. Around a campfire. With no evil spirits lurking nearby. But just then it didn't matter whether Hulk Hogan was headbutting someone into submission or Doris Day was singing "Que será, será." I was hooked.

So began a series of trips to Utshimassits and Sheshashui in search of stories. Almost every elder I visited seemed to have his own special repertoire. I heard origin stories. *Mistapeo* (shaman) stories. Cannibal stories. Tchakapesh stories. Scatological stories. Stories about humans and animals getting married. *Lots* of those. For in a hunting culture, marrying an animal is the natural extension of a hunter's hope and desire that game will give itself to him.

I became a kind of hunter-gatherer myself. Once in a while I'd return home emptyhanded, as when an elder with a scantiness of tooth informed me that a White Man couldn't possibly understand an Innu *atnukan* (story) and in any event he was too senile, he said, to remember one. More often, I would get enough for a

feast, as when one man reeled off the entire Tchakapesh cycle in a single sitting. Occasionally I'd get
enough for a feast and a visit to the lavatory both, as
when one fine summer's day I dropped in on a storyteller, Apinam Ashini, deep in his spruce beer cups. He
was standing rather haphazardly among the animal
bones, flip-tops, rancid caribou skins, and disem-
bowelled mattresses of his front yard. A purist might
take exception to all this trash, but it's probably unfair
to demand a suburban lawn ethic from a man whose
people had no fixed abodes until a generation ago.

AA: *"Ehe!* They say God made the world. I think
Kwakwadjec, Wolverine, made it. I *know* he did. My
grandfather told me so. He put his lips to a muskrat's
ass and … blew. Out came the world."

LM: "Your grandfather put his lips to a muskrat's
ass??"

AA: "No, Kwakwadjec. That's why the world is so
much shit."

LM: "Well, maybe your people ought to be worship-
ping him Sunday mornings. Maybe the priest ought to
be saying something like, Our Kwakwadjec Who art in
Heaven …"

AA: "But Kwakwadjec is *not* in heaven. He's here,
around here. Some twenty years ago, I saw him myself
in a shaking tent on the Goose River. He danced
around and he farted. Farted for, oh, two hours. Kwakwadjec was a great farter, friend. And a great one for
poking his penis into *matweuns* …"

Part of this was Apinam's spruce beer talking. But
another part is the unabashed ribaldry of The People.
In their language, references to bodily functions and
the genitalia carry no moral or immoral connotation
whatsoever. Smut is White Man's invention, not theirs.
As far back as 1634, Father Paul le Jeune, in his *Jesuit*

As far back as 1634, Father Paul le Jeune, in his *Jesuit Relation,* complained: "In place of saying, through wonder, 'Jesus! what is that?' or 'My God! who has done that?', these vile and infamous people [the Innu] pronounce the names of the private parts of man and woman. Their lips are constantly foul with these obscenities, and it is the same with the little children ..."
Innu stories tend to be just as ribald as the Innu themselves. Let me interject a brief polemic:
One of the myriad injustices perpetrated by White Man on the Indian is the theft of his lore and the subsequent whitewashing of it for puritans of all shapes and denominations. Especially puritan parents eager for prematurely puritan offspring. Cleaned up versions of Indian stories with much too cute drawings line the mythology/folklore shelves of libraries and bookstores. On those shelves, the well-endowed Ojibwa trickster Nanabozho seems to have lost his organ of generation. Coyote, the Hopi-Navaho culture hero, ends up losing his divinely-ordained ability to shit whenever and wherever he pleases. Even Wolverine has found himself airbrushed a couple of times. All because earthiness and scatology run counter to White Man's romantic image—romantic *and* patronizing—of the Indian as a brave, clean, sexless Child of Nature. Thus censored, the Indian becomes a sort of Bambi in Native drag, very, very unthreatening.
A good many of the stories I heard would have brought a blush to Father le Jeune's virginal cheeks. Others that are dirt-free might have disturbed the good Father owing to their triumphantly heathen point of view. Yet whether they're scatological or hygienic, Innu stories were not invented to entertain the Jesuits. The Innu themselves believe their stories originated in dreams, particularly dreams brought on by fasting or

mega-doses of grease before bedtime. To dream is an essential aspect of Innu life. Even today a person will go to sleep and, upon waking, narrate his dreams to whoever happens to be around; if there's no one around, he'll tell them to the family dog. Anything to avoid the bad luck likely to bedevil a hoarder of dreams. From telling a dream to telling an *atnukan*— that's perhaps a difference Time and a bit of license will take care of quite nicely.

Bad as it is not to tell your dreams, it's even worse not to act on them. You risk becoming a target for the most abysmal luck of all: death. I heard about an Utshimassits man who ignored his dreams, always refused to heed their advice, and who happened to step into a fox trap. When his body was found, it'd been nibbled to shreds by, it was assumed, foxes.

One day I was hanging around Sheshashui—trying to buy some snowshoes, I think—when an elder approached me and said. "I dreamed about you last night. I dreamed you were coming to my house tonight."

I gathered the man had spent much of the morning tracking me down. Which wasn't easy, given his lame, arthritic hobble and a generally hungover condition. But Innu custom obliged him, nay, *forced* him to invite me to his house even if he hated my guts. I wonder what would have happened if I had refused to go there. Would the unfulfilled dream have revenged itself on him? Or would it have revenged itself on *me?* Anyway, I accepted the invitation and the man in question, John Michel, turned out to be just the sort of person I was looking for, a veritable fountain of stories and old lore. He knew cures, too. I'll always cherish his backwoods cure for a cavity: put a little gunpowder in the offending tooth and then a match to it and BANG! the cavity's gone.

anywhere so devoted to their dreams as the Innu. They put the other dream-obsessed Algonquins to shame.

JM: "All right, I'll tell you something. A person is born empty. Dreams fill him. It's just like you've got a skidoo. A skidoo can't go anywhere unless it's filled with petrol, can it?"

LM: "What about someone who hardly dreams at all? Like me?"

JM: "Why he'd be no better than a *bokageesh*. A black fly."

And so The People dream the century to its conclusion. They dream stories, they dream the whereabouts of game, and they've even been known to dream a *bokageesh* like me. Yet what they won't be able to dream, I fear, is a future worthy of their own admittedly severe past. That past tilted them from one hardship to the next, one lean year to the next, and occasionally tilted them right into the lap of starvation. But at least it gave them a specific *raison d'etre:* Find some bloody food! Today they're beset by a multiplicity of bugaboos which, taken together, are worse, much worse than the specter of starvation—rampant alcoholism, glue sniffing, low-flying NATO jets, hydro projects despoiling their land, recreational hunters killing their caribou, huge clear-cuts in their forests, and young people increasingly lost to White Man's peculiar ways. This is not the stuff dreams are made of. Rather, it's the stuff of an impoverished sleep, the sleep of the woolly mammoth, an eternal sleep.

... with a quick flutter of his hands, Thomas Pastitshi ends the telling of his Wolverine tale. The tent, briefly a palace, is once again only a wind-shipped heap of canvas, a small, lonely beacon in the immense subarctic night.

As this book goes to press, the author has learned that the Innu and Utshimassits will be resettled by the Canadian government to an as yet undetermined location.

Note: Like other macro-Algonquin languages, Inueimun leans heavily on verbs and verb constructions. Whereas an English speaker might say, "It's lousy weather," a speaker of Inueimun would say, "It-lousy-weathers." That sort of tortured syntax is fine in the original, but not much fun to read in translation. It has the additional drawback of making one's Indian friends sound demented. So I've chosen a more or less standard vernacular for my renderings of Innu stories. I've also pruned a bit here, reshaped a bit there, and omitted most localisms. And I confess I even fused together two or more versions of the same story on occasion. Anything that would help transport the reader to distant Labrador and, once there, squat him down next to a voluble Innu elder.

I. WOLVERINE THE TRICKSTER

Wolverine Creates The World

Long, long ago was a time of great floods. Almost the whole world lay underwater. Wolverine was able to keep dry only by leaping from stone to stone. He said to himself: If these floods get any worse, even my stepping stones will be submerged and that'll put an end to my wandering, perhaps my life, too.

So he called a meeting of all the water animals. He asked each to help him save the world from drowning.

First he talked to Otter. "Dive down, Otter," Wolverine said, "and bring me some ground."

Otter dived down, but he came up without any ground. He said he couldn't see anything down there except weeds and a few fish.

Next he talked to Beaver. He said: "If you bring up some ground, I will find a pretty little wife for you."

Beaver also went down, but he didn't bring back any ground, either. "I can't swim deep enough to reach the bottom," he gasped, "and as for a wife, I'd rather live without one than drown."

So Wolverine asked Muskrat to bring him some ground. "I'll try," Muskrat said, "but only if you tie a thong to my leg."

The thong was tied and Muskrat jumped into the water. He was down there for quite a while. I hope he didn't drown, Wolverine thought. He pulled up the rope and when he did, up came the thong ... without Muskrat.

Too bad, thought Wolverine. That means only water, water, and more water from now on.

But just when he had given up, Muskrat surfaced. His mouth was so full of ground that he couldn't talk. Nor could he breathe. Wolverine put his lips to Muskrat's ass and blew as hard as he could. Out came the ground from Muskrat's mouth, more and more ground, heaps and heaps of it, seemingly without end.

This ground is the very earth we walk on today.

How Rocks Were Born

Once upon a time there weren't any rocks in the world, only one very large boulder. Wolverine went over to this boulder and said: "I bet I can outrun you, friend."

To which the boulder replied: "That's probably true, for I can't run at all. In fact, I've been sitting in this same place for as long as I can remember."

"Can't run? But even Lemming can run. Even Ant can do it. You must be the lowest of the low, friend."

And with that, Wolverine gave the boulder a strong kick. The boulder did not like this kick, or Wolverine's insults, so it began rolling toward him.

"Well, at least you can *move,"* Wolverine laughed, and he took off down a hill with the boulder rolling after him.

"Are you pleased now?" the boulder said.

"I am, but I wish you'd slow down. You're hurting my heels."

"I thought you wanted to see me run ..."

Suddenly Wolverine fell down and the boulder rolled right on top of him. "Get off! You're breaking my body!" he yelled. But the boulder just sat there and went on breaking his body.

Now Wolverine called on his brothers to help him.

"Wolf, get rid of this damn boulder!"

"Fox, get rid of this damn boulder!"

Neither Wolf nor Fox would help him. They said it

was only fair, since he'd insulted the boulder, that he be stuck under it.

"Frog, come here and help me get rid of this boulder!"

Frog tried to lift the boulder, but his hands were so slippery that he couldn't move it at all.

"Mouse, can you help me?"

"Sorry, brother," said Mouse, "but I'm too small."

At last Wolverine called on his brother Thunderstorm. Thunderstorm took one look at him and roared with laughter. "What are you doing under that boulder, brother?"

"Being silly again," sighed Wolverine. "Now will you please help me get up?"

Thunderstorm called on Lightning, who zigzagged down from the sky and struck the boulder BAMM! It broke into many, many little pieces.

That's how rocks were born.

From then on, Wolverine said only kind things to these rocks.

He did not want his body broken again.

Why Certain Creatures Live In Rotten Tree Stumps

Wolverine was searching around for a hunting partner. He came to a place where two women, a mother and her daughter, had put up their camp. The daughter said she would hunt with him.

"But you're a woman."

"Not really. It's just that someone has been conjuring with me and now I look like this."

"If you're a man," Wolverine said, "let's see you piss."

She squatted down.

"Just as I thought," Wolverine said. And he wandered on. But wherever he wandered, he couldn't seem to find a man who would hunt with him. Indeed, he couldn't find a man—any kind of man—in all the world. He thought to himself: Maybe men haven't been made yet. That's something for me to do one of these days.

But he still needed a hunting partner. So he went back to the womens' camp. "Pack up your things," he told the women, "and come with me."

The first night Wolverine offered the women caribou heads for supper. The daughter took her head and tried to pull apart the jaws. She kept pulling and pulling until she pulled so hard that she fell over on her back.

"*Ehe!*" Wolverine exclaimed. "I can see you're not a man." And he leaped right on top of her.

"Don't let him do that," said the mother to her daughter. "You'll have a baby and then you won't be able to hunt at all."

But the girl had already stuck Wolverine's penis between her legs. The old woman grabbed the penis from her. "I'm your mother," she said, sticking it between her own legs, "so I'm supposed to go first." When she'd finished, the daughter took it and stuck it back between her legs. And when she'd finished, the old woman grabbed it again.

Next morning Wolverine got up early to go hunting. As the two women were still asleep, he decided to hunt by himself. But he was so tired from the night before that he only got as far as a little clearing near his tent. Then he lay down on the moss and fell asleep.

Along came a spider, a caterpillar, and an ant. They saw Wolverine's penis sticking up in the air. The spider took a whiff of it and said: "There's a woman around here somewhere."

"A woman! A woman!" shouted the others and off they all went to find her.

A while later Wolverine woke up. What's my blanket doing in the sky? he said to himself. Then he realized his penis was holding it up there. "Little brother," he said to the penis, "it seems as if you would like some more work ... even after last night." So he returned to the two women in the tent.

The women were stretched out asleep, as before. Wolverine started to wake them, but then he noticed the spider, the caterpillar, and the ant crawling in and out of their vaginas. And as they crawled, they sang: What a sweet taste! How lovely! We can't get enough of it!

Wolverine reached down and seized all three of them.

"Hey! Why did you do that, short-legs?" they cried.

"Because creatures like you aren't allowed in womens' vaginas, that's why," Wolverine said, adding: "You want a place to crawl? Well, I'll give you a place to crawl."

Whereupon he flung them into the stump of a rotten tree.

"That's where you'll be living from now on, friends," he said.

And in rotten tree stumps all three of them have lived to this very day.

Tciwetinowinu

One winter Wolverine was wandering through slush. Everywhere he went, he'd sink up to his thighs in this slush. He couldn't cross rivers because there was never enough ice on them. Nor could he cross lakes because there was always too much water on the ice. At last he said:

"What's wrong with Tciwetinowinu? If he really wants to prove himself a man, he ought to send a real winter."

A while later Wolverine came upon an enormous man dressed entirely in white. The man said, "I'm Tciwetinowinu. I hear you're not satisfied with the weather."

Wolverine repeated what he'd said about the winter not being cold enough.

Tciwetinowinu smiled. "I'll see what I can do," he said.

Next summer it was very warm. Fall was also warm. Winter started out like it was going to be warm, too.

Tciwetinowinu is a woman, thought Wolverine.

Then snow started coming down in thick clumps, and Wolverine's camp was buried. Also, it grew very cold.

One day Tciwetinowinu dropped by for a visit. Wolverine's teeth were rattling, his feet were nearly frozen, but he would not let on that he was cold.

"How do you like this weather, friend?" Tciwetinowinu asked.

"It's all right," Wolverine said, "but I was hoping for something a little colder."

Next day the snow came down in even thicker clumps. Then the snow stopped and it grew so cold that branches were snapping off trees. Wolverine sat in front of his fire, pouring grease on it. Tciwetinowinu dropped by for another visit.

"How do you like the weather now?"

As before, Wolverine would not give in. Instead he began to tell his guest all the gossip he'd heard that year. Who'd stolen the most wives and that sort of thing. And as he talked, he kept pouring grease on the fire.

Tciwetinowinu was beginning to melt. On and on Wolverine gossiped, even as his guest was melting away.

At last Tciwetinowinu said: "You're stronger than I am, friend. You have beaten me at my own tricks. There's nothing for me to do now but say goodbye."

He walked out of Wolverine's tent and the very moment he left, the cold became less severe.

And so it is that ever since that time, winters have been winters, neither too cold or too hot, just right.

The Giant Skunk

One day a giant skunk came to a camp and sprayed two old women. One of the women said to the other: "That's a mighty powerful fart you've got there, sister."

"I haven't farted, sister. But your fart is a killer …"

And soon both women were dead from the smell.

Now the skunk moved on to where a man was frying bear fat to make oil. The man said to himself: This fat smells real bad. *Kue!* I seem to smell bad myself …

Before long, he was dead, too.

Through the camp went the skunk, spraying women and children, babies and old people, even dogs. Whoever got sprayed fell dead in his tracks. At last only the headman and his two sons were left alive. The headman said: "We must get our brother Wolverine to help us. Otherwise, we'll die, too."

So they visited Wolverine in his den. "I've killed wolves, bears, even human beings themselves," said Wolverine, "so I can easily get rid of a mere skunk."

But when Wolverine saw all those dead bodies, he changed his mind. Too late! The giant skunk was already advancing toward him. Suddenly it turned around and aimed its ass at his face. Wolverine clamped down his jaws directly on the skunk's ass and kept them clamped, knowing that if he let go, the skunk would release its fumes and he'd die.

Now the headman and his sons came out from their hiding place. "Good job, Wolverine, old friend!" they said. Then they began hitting the skunk's head with their clubs. They hit its head again and again until it collapsed on the ground. Wolverine eased his jaws. And just before the skunk died, it sprayed him in the face.

"It got me! It got me!" Wolverine cried.

He ran right down to the sea and jumped in. There he washed himself until he'd managed to wash off all the smell ... into the sea.

And ever since Wolverine washed there, sea water has smelled bad, tasted bad, and been of no use whatsoever to anyone.

Why Muskrats Don't Eat Rocks

Wolverine saw Char swimming in the water, so he bent down and said to him: "Salmon was been telling me some awful things about you, brother."

"What sort of awful things?"

"Well, he said you swam into Muskrat's ass. And you liked it so much that you went back and did it again."

"Salmon should talk," Char said. "He can't even make love to his wife without dying ..."

Wolverine went to Salmon and told him what Char had said. Salmon replied, "Every time Char farts, the smell drives me up a river. Tell him that."

Now Wolverine went back and forth, back and forth, getting the two of them angrier and angrier with each other. At last they decided to fight it out, with Wolverine as referee.

"This has to be a fight to the death," Wolverine said. "The one who's the winner must have killed the loser."

Salmon and Char killed each other.

That was exactly what Wolverine had been hoping for. He cut both of them open, took out the meat, boiled it, and then dried it. What a wonderful life this is, he said to himself. He put all the meat in his gamebag and feel asleep.

Muskrat saw him sleeping there. Ah, he said, it's my dear brother Wolverine. So I entertain guests in my ass, do I? Well, I think I'll play a little trick on him.

Muskrat took the dried meat from Wolverine's game-bag and replaced it with rocks.

After a long sleep, Wolverine woke up. He was very hungry, so he reached for his gamebag. Raised it to his mouth. Chewed. Swallowed. "Toughest meat I've ever eaten," he exclaimed. Then he emptied the rest of the gamebag into his mouth, adding: "But it does have a rather interesting flavor ..."

Muskrat was watching all this from behind a tree. Anything a great hunter like Wolverine ate, he figured he could eat, too. So he gathered a batch of rocks and tossed them into his mouth. His teeth splintered and fell out, and he ended up with the worst stomach ache of his life.

Muskrat never ate rocks again.

Why Shrews Are Shrews

O nce Wolverine drank from a waterhole for such a long time that his mouth froze to the ice. None of his friends could find a way to get him loose.

Too bad, brother, Wolf told him, but I'm afraid you'll have to stay like that until spring thaw.

Um-m-m, um-m-m, replied Wolverine, for he couldn't talk with a frozen mouth.

Then a couple of shrews came along. Right away they saw what the problem was, so they went to work with their sharp little teeth. In almost no time Wolverine was free from the ice.

I promise I'll never hunt you again, brothers, Wolverine told them.

But, as usual, he didn't keep his promise.

Which is why shrews have such a reputation for shrewishness: they don't trust anyone except their fellow shrews.

Wolverine Flies

One day Wolverine saw a flock of geese flying across the sky. If geese can fly, he told himself, I ought to be able to fly, too. He flapped his front paws, but nothing seemed to happen. He flapped them again, but nothing happened again. So he visited some geese and asked them to teach him how to fly.

The geese dressed him with feathers, gave him a pair of wings no one was using, and soon he was flying just like a goose.

"You must beware of human beings, brother," the geese told him, "for they will kill you if they see you."

Said Wolverine: "I haven't been afraid of human beings before, and I won't start being afraid of them now."

So he flew as he pleased until he flew over a camp. Down in this camp he saw an old woman. Ah, he said, it's one of those stupid human beings. And he shouted: *Stupid human being! Stupid human being!*

The old woman took up her bow and shot an arrow which went right through one of Wolverine's wings. While he was trying to shake loose this arrow, she shot an arrow into his other wing. He plummeted down to where the old woman was standing. She dropped her leggings and squatted over him, saying:

"I've always wanted to shit on a wolverine."

Wolverine said to her: "Don't shit on me, grandmother! I'll find you a partridge for supper, a hare, anything, only don't shit on me!"

The old woman shat all over him.

That's when Wolverine decided to give up flying.

So it was told long ago.

How Wolverine Got Stuck In A Bear's Skull

For a long time Wolverine had eaten only lemmings and shrews. He craved fat, real fat, with lots of grease. So when he noticed a big she-bear prowling around, he formed a plan to get her into his stewpot.

"How are you doing, sister?" he said.

"Why are you calling me sister?" the bear replied. "I'm a bear and you're a wolverine, two entirely different creatures."

"A wolverine? Your eyesight seems to be failing you, sister. I'm a bear just like you. Indeed, I'm your brother."

"Your legs are too short for you to be a bear."

"Admit it, sister. You're losing your eyesight. Why, I bet you can't even see that patch of ripe berries over there."

He pointed to a barren hillside.

"I see only moss and rock ..."

Now Wolverine conjured berries all over the hillside. The two of them went over there. The bear exclaimed: "How did your eyes get to be so good?"

Said Wolverine: "Our father used to squeeze berry juice into my eyes. And as everyone knows, berry juice improves the eyesight."

"Think you could squeeze some into my eyes?"

"I'll be glad to, sister. But first you must lie down."

The bear did as she was told.

"Next, you must remember this: your eyes will get worse before they get any better."

"I'll remember, brother."

And so Wolverine began squeezing berries into the bear's eyes. The juice blinded her.

"You're doing fine, just fine, sister," he said. He grabbed his lance and pierced her heart with it.

That was almost too easy, he said to himself.

After Wolverine had dressed the bear's carcass, he got an urge to eat the brains. Usually he left brains for dessert, but now all he wanted to do was crack the skull and eat them. However, the skull would not crack. Even when he threw it against a rock, it wouldn't crack.

Well, he thought, I'll just have to conjure myself into a maggot.

That's exactly what he did. Then he crawled right in through an eye-socket and began sucking on the brains. He sucked ... and sucked ... and sucked. And grew bigger ... and bigger ... and bigger.

At last Wolverine was such a big maggot that he couldn't crawl out of the eye-socket.

"Help!" he cried. "I'm trapped inside a bear's skull!"

But no help came. For who would ever want to help a maggot?

I suppose I'll starve to death now, Wolverine thought.

But he didn't starve to death. Instead he got thinner and thinner until he was thin enough to crawl out the eye-socket. Once he was out of the socket, he got back his old shape again. And not having eaten since he ate the last of the brains, he was now very hungry.

It's a good thing I have all that bear meat, Wolverine told himself.

But where was this bear meat? He couldn't seem to find it anywhere. He even peered under rocks to see if he'd cached it, but it was nowhere to be seen. That's because a wolf had found the meat and dragged it off while Wolverine was stuck inside the skull.

So now Wolverine went back to eating lemmings and shrews.

And he never conjured himself into a maggot again.

Wolverine Eats His Own Ass

Once it happened that Wolverine couldn't stop farting. And these farts were scaring away all the game. "Shut up!" he told his ass.

"You shut up," his ass replied, "or else stop eating so much moss. That's why you're farting all the time."

"No, *you're* why I'm farting all the time, friend, and I'm going to punish you for it."

So he heated a large stone and sat down on it until he'd burned his ass to a reddish crisp.

"You're killing me!" cried the ass.

"Maybe that will teach you not to fart when I'm trying to hunt," Wolverine said.

Over the next few days his ass began to heal and one of the scabs fell off. Ah, thought Wolverine, a piece of dried meat. Just my luck that someone dropped it. He picked up the scab and ate it, saying, Um-m-m, not bad at all ... Later another scab fell off and he ate that one, too. And then another. And another.

Now came a bad winter, with very little game. But Wolverine, as always, was resourceful: he survived this winter by eating his own ass.

Or so the old people used to say.

How Wolverine Tried To Destroy The World

And so Wolverine made the world. But once he tried to get rid of it. I'll tell you about that:

It was winter, and very cold. Wolverine didn't have any wood, so he was burning bones for their fat. Then he ran out of bones, too. Well, he said, maybe I can find some sort of female who'll keep me warm. A while later a pretty young girl showed up at his camp. Wolverine said to himself: I'll get under her dress tonight. He invited her to share some caribou hearts with him. Only if you cook them, she said. I don't have any wood, he replied: no bones, either. Well, she told him, if you won't cook them, I'm not going to eat them. And off she went on her snowshoes. Now Wolverine was so angry that he started tearing up the earth, grabbing it and throwing pieces into the sky. Most of these pieces just came back down again ... they're the mountains. But some stayed up there forever. That's the Milky Way.

Isn't it wonderful how things came about?

II. ODD COUPLES

Amusk

There was a man, Amusk, whom every animal seemed to desire. First a fox asked to marry him.

"Let's see how you put up a camp," Amusk told her. The fox dug a nice, warm underground camp. Amusk moved in all his gear. Next morning he woke up to find that the fox had eaten his moccasins, his snowshoes, and his hauling rope.

"Sorry," he told her, "but I can't marry a woman who eats my gear."

Then a caribou approached him, saying: "I'd like to marry you, Amusk."

"All right," said Amusk, "I'll watch you put up a camp."

The caribou made a lovely camp, all white, out of caribou moss. Only trouble was, she ate the camp almost immediately after she put it up.

"Too bad," said Amusk, "but I can't have a wife who's always eating my home."

Next he was visited by a porcupine. She made a quite comfortable camp, mostly from tree bark, and Amusk invited her to spend the night there with him. Next morning, however, he sent her on her way, saying:

"Sorry, dear. I can't marry a woman who leaves her quills in my penis."

A while later Amusk had a dream in which a beaver appeared to him and asked to be his wife. To disobey such a dream would bring very bad luck, so he set out to find the beaver. At last he found her in a lodge beside Nipishish Lake. She was a handsome animal with a rich brown coat and a fine scaly tail. Amusk married her.

One day Amusk's wife told him: "Every time we cross a stream, you'll have to put down branches. All beavers do that. You too must do it ... if you want to stay married to me."

Now Amusk started putting down branches across even the smallest streams.

Another day the beaver said: "From now on, we must live in the water."

"But I can't live in the water," Amusk told her. "I'll freeze."

"Try it anyway. Here, take off your clothes."

Amusk took off his clothes and lo! the water did not feel cold at all.

In time Amusk and the beaver had four children: all beavers. Amusk loved these children very much, but no less did he love his wife ... even though she'd occasionally slap his face with her tail when he forgot about the branches.

One night Amusk's brother, a *mistapeo,* dreamed about him. "I wonder where Amusk has gone," the brother asked the dream. And the dream showed him the lodge beside Nipishish Lake.

Now the brother journeyed to this lodge. Once there, he started banging on his drum. As he banged, one by one Amusk's children swam out into the open water.

And not knowing they were his first cousins, the brother killed them with his spear.

"What's happened to our children?" Amusk's wife cried. And when she went out to find them, the brother killed her, too. Then he entered the lodge where he saw Amusk, completely naked, hunched in a corner. "Take these, brother," he said, and conjured clothes onto Amusk's body.

"I'd rather be a beaver than a human being," Amusk protested.

"That's not such a good idea," his brother said, "unless you fancy being hunted for your meat, your pelt, or your glands."

"All right, brother," Amusk said. "I'll go back with you. But one favor I'd like to request: Never put the gravy of a female beaver in front of me."

"I promise to honor your request, dear Amusk."

So it was that Amusk returned to his brother's camp. Before long he was just like a man again … except he would not marry. Human females, he'd say, smelled bad. What's more, they always wore clothing so it was impossible to see their best parts.

Some years later Amusk's brother happened to trap a female beaver. He cooked up a haunch from this beaver and then covered it all over with gravy. Old Amusk will never know what animal this is, he thought to himself: Besides, we don't have any other meat.

Amusk took a piece of the meat. "What am I eating, brother?" he asked.

"Muskrat," came the reply.

All of a sudden a cool stream began flowing from under Amusk. It gathered force and he was carried right out of the tent with it. The brother followed this stream through the woods to a large lake. And there, in the water, he saw a male beaver and a female beaver swimming side by side.

Amusk and his wife were back together again, forever.

A Woman And Her Dog

Just south of Utshimassits, the three of them lived—a man, a woman, and a dog. One winter the man got the burning sickness and died. The woman was fearful that she would die herself, since there was no one to look after her now.

"Don't worry," the dog told her. "I'll look after you."

And the dog did look after her, too. Each day he'd put on her husband's snowshoes and hunt game for her stewpot. Evenings he'd stroke her hair ... just like her husband used to stroke it. He also seemed to know about taboos, for once when she was getting ready to eat a bear's heart, he stopped her, saying, "No, dear, that's a man's food ..."

One day the woman dropped her leggings and asked him how he liked her ass. The dog replied: "Well, it's prettier than a she-dog's ass, that's for sure."

Soon they were living together as man and wife.

Now a year of moons passed. The muskrat moon, the duck moon, the falling-leaves moon, and back to the muskrat moon again. One evening a robust young hunter walked into their camp while the woman was dressing a caribou carcass.

"You have a husband, woman?" the hunter asked her.

"My husband is dead."

"Then where did you get that caribou?"

"Oh, it's just something the dog dragged in ..."

The woman and the hunter spent the night curled up

together in her tent. The dog slept outside, as in the old days.

Next morning the hunter left early. The dog flung back the tent flap and there was the woman lying naked on her back. When she saw him, she turned over and smiled: How do you like my ass, dear? Whereupon the dog jumped on her and bit her all over her back and thighs, her ass, too.

"Maybe you'll be faithful to me now," he said.

And she was faithful to him from then on.

Soon there were puppies.

Niassa

Two girls were paddling a canoe across a lake. One of them took off her neck amulet and flung it in the water. "Why did you do that?" asked the other girl, whose name was Niassa.

"To appease Amiskuapeu ..."

"Master Beaver? You don't believe that silly stuff, do you?"

"I believe in all the masters. Master Marten, Master Bear, Master Wolf, Master Owl ..."

"How about a Master Leech?" Niassa laughed.

Suddenly a huge leech stuck its head from the water. It grabbed Niassa and carried her to the bottom of the lake, where it proceeded to mate with her.

And that's how Niassa became Mrs. Leech.

Moral: Respect the masters, friend, or you'll be sorry.

Petabanu The Bachelor

Once a man named Petabanu went fishing. He made all the right prayers to Missinaku, Master of Fish, so he caught half a dozen char with only half a dozen flings of his line. All but one of these char he roasted for his supper. This last one he saved for breakfast.

That evening Petabanu checked his traps. When he returned to his tent, he found a lovely young woman on his sleeping skins.

"Who are you?" he asked.

"I am called One-Who-Wiggles-Nicely."

"Where do you come from, One-Who-Wiggles-Nicely?"

"From the lake where you've just been fishing."

Now the woman was taking off his leggings. "It is whispered that you want a wife," she said.

"It is whispered correctly."

Petabanu lay down with One-Who-Wiggles-Nicely. After they'd mated, he slept. All night he dreamed he was swimming around with a bunch of fish. When he woke up, the woman was nowhere to be seen.

"Ishkue! Ishkue!" he shouted. "Please come back!"

But the woman did not come back.

Such is the lot of the bachelor, Petabanu mused. But at least I won't have to share my last char with another person.

So he took down the char from the tent pole, roasted

it and ate it. As soon as he did this, he heard a woman's voice cry out from inside his stomach:

"You ate me ..."

He tried to ignore this voice, but it just cried louder:

"You ate me, Petabanu. How could you do such a thing?"

It was One-Who-Wiggles-Nicely, of course. And from then on, she was always there, always inside his stomach, crying:

"You ate me! You ate me! And you said you loved me, too!"

Why Martens Live In The Deep Forest

There was once a marten who fell in love with a hunter's wife. Each time the man left her alone, the marten would slip into her tent and they would make love. Once, however, the man came back early and caught the two of them together. He was so angry that he picked up a kettle and threw boiling water onto the marten. Out of the tent ran the marten, screaming in pain, and he did not stop running until he reached the deepest part of the forest. And that's where martens live to this very day: they're still afraid husbands will throw boiling water at them.

The Lemming And The Shit

Once a lemming saw a piece of shit lying on a rock. He said: "You smell bad, really bad, Brother Shit. It makes me sick to get downwind of you."

To think—insulted by a lemming! The shit was so upset by this that it hid its odor, of which it'd been rather proud. Next time the lemming came by, it was only a dried-up greyish turd which had no smell at all.

Moral: Be true to yourself, friend, or you'll die.

Puan Takes A Lover

A woman named Puan was married to a hunter who never brought home enough game. He'd come back with a pair of half-starved squirrels, maybe a partridge or two, and tell Puan that was enough.

Once the man brought back a skinny little snowshoe hare.

"Our children are hungry, husband," Puan told him.

"Let them eat this snowshoe hare," the man declared. "If it's good enough for a lynx, it's good enough for them."

That night Puan had a dream. In this dream, a handsome young man stepped out of a dead tree and told her that she had splendid loins. Your loins are rather nice themselves, she said. The two of them mated all through the dream.

Several days later Puan was sewing bark on a new canoe. She did not have enough spruce roots to tie on this bark, so she went into the forest to dig a few more. All at once she saw the dead tree from her dream. Puan thought: Inside this tree lives my lover. So she searched the rotten wood until she found … a snake!

The snake said: "You have splendid loins, woman. Perhaps you'd like to mate?"

Puan said she wasn't too keen about mating with a snake.

"I'll give you meat," he told her.

My children are hungry, Puan thought, and here's

this snake offering me some meat. It would be wrong to turn him down.

So Puan allowed the snake to crawl under her dress. He was down there for quite a while. When he came out, he said: "I like the taste of you, woman."

Now Puan would visit the snake whenever her husband went out hunting. And each time she visited him, she would bring back meat, real meat, for her children.

One day her husband returned earlier than usual and saw his children eating this meat. He knew something was wrong. *Where did you get that meat?* he demanded.

"Don't you think I'm able to hunt by myself?" Puan said.

Next morning the man left with his bow and lance. But instead of going off to hunt, he followed his wife to the tree. He heard her say: "I'm ready, dear." And he saw the snake crawl out of the tree and under her dress.

Aha, he said, my little wife seems to have found a lover.

The man returned to camp and got out one of his wife's dresses. That evening he put on the dress and visited the tree himself, saying: "Would you like to crawl into me tonight, dear?"

The snake crawled out of the tree. Suddenly the man took his axe and chopped it in half. Then he chopped at these halves until he'd chopped them into dozens of little pieces. Now, he said to himself, we'll see how my wife likes *this* meat.

Back in camp the man threw the pieces of the snake into a stewpot. Then he cooked them in their own blood and served them to Puan. "Um-m-m," she said. "This tastes good. What is it?"

"Can you guess?"

"Is it from a yearling caribou?"

"No."

"Beaver tail?"

"No."

"I give up."

"Well, it's your lover the snake!" the man said.

Whereupon Puan vomited up everything she'd eaten. All the pieces of the snake became little snakes, which immediately crawled onto her and her children. When they crawled away again, Puan wasn't there anymore. Her children were gone, too.

"My family has been stolen by snakes!" the man cried, beating his fists on the ground.

He was alone, all alone now.

That's what happens to husbands who don't bring their wives enough meat.

Atiskan

A woman had too many babies, so she left behind one of them to die. It was found by a mouse who couldn't have any offspring herself. The mouse took in the baby and raised it as her own, calling it Atiskan.

When Atiskan grew to manhood, he wanted to marry.

"Why don't you marry a mouse?" the mouse said.

"No, mother," he told her. "Since I'm a human being, I want a human woman."

One day Atiskan happened to meet a porcupine. I wonder if that's a woman, he said to himself. So he slept with the porcupine and ended up with quills all over his body.

Next he met a female wolf. Maybe *that's* a woman, Atiskan said. But when the wolf tried to bite off his penis, he decided not to marry her.

At last he came upon a human woman. "Will you marry me?" he asked her. "No," she replied, "for you walk and talk just like a mouse. You smell like a mouse, too."

Poor Atiskan! He never married.

Utshisk Lake

Two beautiful girls lived on the shore of Utshisk Lake. Not only were these girls beautiful, they were also very haughty. If a man came to court them, they would kick his canoe back in the lake, saying, "We're simply too good for the likes of you, so get lost, dog-face."

One day an unusually handsome man paddled his canoe up to their lodge. Instead of kicking his canoe away, the girls helped him bring it ashore. For he was the most handsome man they'd ever seen.

"Either of you girls interested in marriage?" the man asked.

"Of course!" both of them smiled together.

The man took the older girl to wife. He propped her in his canoe and off they paddled across the lake.

It wasn't long before he returned alone. "What happened to my sister?" the younger girl said.

"Drowned in the lake, poor thing," the man replied.

"That's a shame," said the girl, trying to look sad. Then she said: "Perhaps you'll marry me now?"

"I've come back here for that very reason," he told her.

And off they paddled. Occasionally the girl would gaze back and chortle to herself about what a handsome fellow she'd married.

All at once a big wind came up and the canoe began taking on water. It kept taking on more and more water. The girl was a little worried. "Don't you think we should head for shore?" she asked her husband.

"You're not afraid, are you?" he said. Now when she looked back again, she saw a very large muskrat in the stern of the canoe.

"Where's the man I married?"

"You married *me,* dear," the muskrat said. And shortly after that, the canoe took on so much water that it capsized. The girl flailed around in the water for a few brief moments, then she drowned.

How strange it is, thought the muskrat, that none of the girls I marry can swim.

Moral: Bad things happen to people too lofty for their own mocassins.

The Wolf Girl And The Otter

Once upon a time a Wolf Girl asked an otter to marry her. The otter replied: "I can't marry someone who always has shit on her ass."

"If you refuse to marry me," the Wolf Girl told him, "I'll kill you."

When he heard this, the otter leaped into the nearest lake. The Wolf Girl waited by this lake until it froze over. There was just one breathing hole. The otter came up only to hear the Wolf Girl's voice: "Will you marry me now?"

"I suppose I'll have to marry you," the otter said, "since I have no wish to be killed."

So the two of them went to live with the Wolf Girl's brothers. Husband, wife, brothers—they all slept in the same tent. The otter thought he and his wife should have a tent of their own. "Not until you prove yourself a hunter," the brothers told him.

I'll show you I'm a hunter," the otter said, "though my method is a little different from yours …"

Next day the brothers took the otter to the caribou grounds. He picked out a big bull and rushed toward it. The bull tried to run away, but the otter slipped into its ass and trampled its heart, thereby killing it. He came out the mouth.

The brothers were rolling on the ground with laughter.

"The caribou's dead," the otter said. "It doesn't matter how I killed it."

Every time they went hunting together, the otter would kill his caribou by slipping into its ass and trampling its heart. And every time that happened, the wolves would roll on the ground with laughter.

"I wish you'd tell your brothers to stop laughing at me," the otter said to his wife. She told them, but they refused to stop. They'd say: "Our brother-in-law swims in caribou shit." Or they'd say: "Our brother-in-law's nose is his *shimagin.*" And then they'd be rolling on the ground again.

Finally the otter couldn't tolerate their ridicule any longer. He packed his gear and left. The Wolf Girl was very upset by this, so she set out looking for him. At last she found him in a little camp by a river. "Please come home with me, dear," she said.

"No," the otter replied. "Your brothers made fun of me once too often. Besides, I'm very happy with my new wife."

He pointed to a female otter.

Whereupon the Wolf Girl burst into tears and, it's said, cried herself to death.

Why Certain Animals Live In The Ground

Once there was a rabbit married to a lemming. The rabbit was a hunter. Every day he would go out to search for game while the little lemming minded the tent. Then came a time when the rabbit could find only enough game for himself. He would catch whatever he could and eat it before he returned home. When he got back, the lemming would ask him: "Any food?" And he would shake his head sadly, saying: "No, dear. Too bad. No food today."

With nothing to eat, the lemming began to get smaller and smaller. One day the rabbit came back and found the tent empty. For the lemming had gotten so small, she just slipped through a crack in the ground. The rabbit felt very bad about this. He thought: I must find my poor little wife and prove to her that I still love her. So he dug a hole in the ground himself, and went to look for the lemming. But he could not seem to find her. Even today he is still looking, deep down in the ground.

The Penis

A girl took a penis for a lover. Soon this penis was forcing her to haul him around in a *tabaskan*. As she hauled, he'd shout: "Faster! Faster! And if you don't shorten your lead, I'll find myself another girl."

Once the girl had to haul him around in a blizzard just because he was in the mood for a ride. Another time, when she didn't haul fast enough, he beat her until she felt her body would break.

One day the penis asked the girl to haul him up the hill north of camp. When she'd done that, he said: "That wasn't nearly as hard as I thought it would be. Let's try the hill south of camp. By the way, your lead is too long."

The girl bent down to shorten her lead. Suddenly she lifted up the *tabaskan* and the penis rolled off. He kept on rolling until he'd rolled down the hillside and into a frozen lake far, far below. He hit the ice with such force that he went right through it.

The girl skipped happily back to camp. I should have dumped that awful penis long ago, she told herself.

Next morning a penis came into her tent. The very same penis she'd dumped down the hillside the day before. He was all covered with frost and looked very angry.

"Try that little trick again, girl," he said, "and I'll kill you."

The girl cried. And then they went for a *tabaskan* ride.

Later the girl paid a visit to her old grandmother. "Granny," she said, "I've got a very cruel lover and I can't seem to get rid of him. What should I do?"

The grandmother brought out a bone-awl. "Try sticking him with this," she said. "That's what I used to do with all the men I didn't like."

That night the penis woke up the girl and asked her for a ride.

"And what if I don't give you one?" she said.

"I'll cut off your fingers one by one ..."

Now the girl brought out the bone-awl and stabbed the penis with it. She stabbed him again. Again. Each time she stabbed him, a bit of grease would dribble out. She licked up some of this grease, saying, "Um-m-m, you taste good. For once."

The penis was writhing in pain on the ground. All at once he looked up and said: "I'm your father, girl. Your dear old father. How could you do such a thing to your own father?"

And then he died.

At last the girl was free.

III. Cannibals

The Cannibal Lynx

A lynx had a great fondness for human women. He'd marry them and, if there was no other food, eat them for his supper. He ate one wife after he was married to her for just two days. Another wife he ate even as they were making love.

After a while women seemed to catch on to the lynx. Maybe it was the way he tested their thighs for meat before he asked them to marry him. Or maybe it was the drool on his lips when they agreed to do so. Whatever the reason, he began to have some difficulty in finding a wife.

At last the lynx found a woman willing to marry him. She had a face like a porcupine's and so many lice on her head that they kept dropping into the stewpot. Yet she left him when he tried to put her at the end of his roasting stick.

Now the lynx was all alone. All alone and very, very hungry. He searched around for game, but he couldn't find any. No woman, either. So he said to himself: Maybe *I'm* good to eat ...

He gnawed off one of his legs and put it on his roasting stick. Once he'd cooked the leg, he took a few cautious bites. Rolled the meat around in his mouth.

Swallowed it. Well, he exclaimed, I don't taste bad at all. He ate the rest of the leg, including the bone.

Next day the lynx cut off the other leg and ate that, too. The day after that, he ate his arm. Then his other arm. Next went his loins, his shoulders, and his intestines.

Finally only one thing was left—his heart.

And he was still hungry.

So he tore out his heart, cooked and ate it.

That was the end of the cannibal lynx.

"Give Me Back My Father"

Aboy was tending camp by himself. He heard a noise like icicles clanking together and out of the woods stepped an *atcen*. It had ice for flesh, claws for feet, and smelled real bad. Also, it drooled blood instead of saliva.

The boy did not know about *atcens*. He simply thought the poor fellow had spent too much time in the woods. He said: "What happened to your lips, friend?"

"I was hungry and chewed them off."

"And your fingers?"

"I chewed them off, too ..."

Now the *atcen* grabbed the boy's arm and felt it. "You're too lean, boy. Much too lean. Get some fat on your bones so I can come back and eat you." And off the *atcen* stalked, pushing back trees as if they were blades of grass.

A while later the boy saw a fire over where his father was trapping beavers. It's father, he thought, roasting beaver meat. So he put on his snowshoes and made his way toward the fire. When he got there, he saw not his father roasting beavers but the *atcen* roasting his father.

"Stop that!" the boy cried.

But the *atcen* did not stop. After it had eaten all of the boy's father, it stalked off again, hissing contentedly.

"You'll pay for that, ice-face," the boy said.

Next day he cut off a couple of his fingers and baited

a trap with them. It wasn't long before he heard the sound of icicles again. The *atcen* was approaching. Then the icicles stopped and there was an angry hiss.

"Let me loose!" the *atcen* said.

"Only if you give me back my father," the boy said.

"It's too late."

"Then it's too late to let you loose, too."

"All right," said the *atcen*, "but don't say I didn't warn you."

Suddenly it opened its mouth and vomited up eyes, hair, and entrails. As they touched the ground, they joined together and became the boy's father. The man was not much different from before ... except he drooled blood.

"Oh, father," exclaimed the boy. "I'm so glad to have you back."

The father embraced his son. As he did so, he took a bite out of the boy's cheek.

"Why did you do that, father?"

"Because I've turned into an *atcen* myself," declared the man.

And he ate every last morsel of his son.

The *Mistapeo* Who
Became A Skeleton

Once upon a time a *mistapeo* fell in love with two sisters, the daughters of a giant. Younger sister said to him: "Watch out for my sister. She'll try to eat you with her vagina."

The *mistapeo* did not believe this. He figured she'd use her mouth, assuming she'd ever want to eat him. Then he happened to see the girl squatting in a willow patch and biting off the heads of willows with her vagina. That's exactly what she'll do to my penis, he thought to himself.

Now elder sister asked the man to sleep with her. "I'll be glad to," he said, "but first I'd like to look at your ass." The girl spread wide her legs and he lit his stone lamp and looked not at her ass but at her vagina. It was full of very sharp teeth.

"Are you ready, dear?" the girl aid.

"I'm ready," he replied. And he shoved the stone lamp hard into her vagina. All the teeth shattered. Soon the girl was dead.

"Father will kill you for that," declared younger sister.

The *mistapeo* smiled. "Not if you kill me first."

"But I don't want to kill the man I love."

"I *want* you to kill me," he told her, "for I have more power when I'm dead than when I'm alive."

He instructed her to cut off all his flesh. Leave the

skeleton in the campfire and put the flesh in a neat pile next to it.

The girl did as she was told.

When the giant came home, he saw all that flesh next to the fire. "How thoughtful, daughter," he said to younger sister. "You've already made supper for me."

Suddenly the skeleton leaped from the fire and thrust his *shimagin* into the giant's chest. The giant did not seem to mind this at all. He grabbed a club and whacked the skeleton with it. But that didn't seem to bother the skeleton, either. They kept thrusting and whacking at each other like this until a whiskey jack flew over their battle site, whistling:

"I know a little secret. The giant's heart is in his thumb. In his thumb, skeleton, and if you cut off the thumb, you'll kill him."

So the skeleton got his knife and cut off the giant's thumb. A great spurt of blood went up in the sky and the giant fell down dead.

Now the skeleton walked over to the fire, picked up his flesh, and put it back on just like he was putting on his clothes. Once again he was a human being. "You see? I'm as good as new," he told younger sister.

The two of them got married.

Younger sister's vagina was just fine.

Mishpun

A hunter named Mishpun was out in the woods. He came upon another man who was more bone than flesh and who said he hadn't eaten in many days. I'll bring him back to camp, Mishpun thought, and feed him. By the time they got back to camp, the man had doubled in size and was solid ice from head to foot.

"You've brought home an *atcen,* husband!" Mishpun's wife said to him.

Mishpun still wanted to be a polite host, so he asked the *atcen* what it would like for supper. Perhaps caribou loins?

"To be honest," the *atcen* said, "I'd prefer the loins of you and your wife ..."

So saying, it leaped on Mishpun and began clawing at his chest. Mishpun reached for his knife. He cut off the *atcen's* head, but the *atcen* merely grinned and put it back on again, saying, "That's not how you kill an *atcen,* friend."

"Then how do you kill an *atcen?*"

"Think I'm stupid? I'm not going to tell you. All I'll say is that it has something to do with heat ..."

Aha, thought Mishpun. And he pushed the *atcen* into the campfire. It melted right down until there was nothing left of it but a little sizzling on the logs.

A while later Mishpun's chest felt icy where the *atcen* had clawed him. He also seemed to be growing taller ... and taller. "Quick!" he yelled to his wife. "Cook the dog!"

"Why should I cook the dog?" his wife asked.

"Because I need hot food inside me! Cook the damn dog!"

So she threw the dog into a stewpot. After it was cooked, Mishpun opened his mouth and poured all the broth down his throat. He waited. Slowly his ice began melting and he started shrinking back to normal. Before long, he was just old Mishpun the hunter again.

How useful dogs are!

The Son-In-Law's Revenge

An *atcen* went hunting with his son-in-law. They trekked to a place where the beavers always sang: We will give ourselves to you! This day, however, the beavers weren't singing at all.

"I will dream of their song," the son-in-law said, and he fell asleep.

The *atcen* never liked his son-in-law, so he decided to put him to sleep forever. He picked up a big rock and dropped it on the man's head. Then he buried the body in the ground.

Back in camp the *atcen's* daughter asked about her husband.

"I forgot to tell you," the *atcen* said. "He drowned."

The girl sat down and cried when she heard this. All day long she cried. She told her father: "The only thing that will make me stop crying is a beaver. Did you bring back a beaver like you promised?"

The *atcen* gave her some muskrats.

"I told you a beaver," she cried.

The *atcen* went back to the hunting place, but he could not dream and thus he couldn't hear the song of the beavers. Once again he returned home with muskrats.

"I WANT A BEAVER!" the girl yelled. "Don't come back home without one."

My daughter is very hard to please, the *atcen* thought: Only way I'll get a beaver is by digging up my son-in-law.

So he returned to the place he'd buried the man and dug him up. "Please come back to life, son-in-law, and help me get a beaver for my daughter," he said.

All at once the man opened his eyes. "I'll be glad to help you," he said, "if you'll just remove this rot from me."

The *atcen* got out his scraper and scraped off the man's rot.

Now the two of them set out to find a beaver for the girl. "I will dream of their song," the son-in-law said. But instead of going to sleep, he took an arrow and shot it at the *atcen*. The *atcen* wondered whether this arrow mightn't have been intended for his head. "Were you aiming for me, son-in-law?" he said.

"No," the man replied. "I wasn't aiming for anything. The arrow slipped."

But after a second arrow narrowly missed him, the *atcen* turned himself into a whiskey jack.

Where has my father-in-law gone? the man said to himself. As he was looking around, he happened to see the whiskey jack flying overhead. The *atcen* had forgotten to turn his nose into a beak, so the nose still looked like an *atcen's* nose, all white and icy. The man took out a third arrow and shot the whiskey jack with it. Afterwards, he burned the bird to dust.

Back in camp the man told his wife the whole story. "I hope you're not mad at me, dear," he said.

"Not at all," the girl told him. "Every time I marry a man, my father kills him. I'm glad to have the old man out of the way."

And so it was that the two of them had a happy marriage from then on ... except when the husband forgot to bring home a beaver.

The Ice Baby

young woman gave birth to an ice baby. Upon seeing it, her husband said: "Chop up the little monster."

"But it's my baby," the woman protested.

"It's also a baby *atcen.* If we don't kill it, it'll kill us."

So they took an axe to their child. CRACK! CRACK! CRACK! went its flesh. Soon they saw another baby, all warm and smiling, beneath the ice baby.

"I hope you don't want to chop up this one," the mother said, cradling it in her arms.

"No," said the father, "this one seems to be normal."

And so they kept the baby, naming it Atshukash, Little Mink.

A year passed. Another year. One day the mother was fondling her Atshukash when he smiled up at her and wrung her neck. Then he walked over to where his father was dressing a caribou carcass and wrung his neck, too.

"I'm sorry, parents, Atshukash said, "but once an *atcen,* always an *atcen.*"

Then the little boy realized he didn't have a mother or a father anymore. Who would help him put on his snowshoes now? Who would strip the fat from intestines for him? Who would fondle him at night?

Poor Atshukash wrung his own neck.

How Manish And His Son Were Killed

Once there lived a pair of cannibals, Manish and his son, who would come to a camp and kill everyone there. Then they'd roast their victims over a slow fire. And then they'd eat them, all but the brains. Human brains, they thought, tasted very bitter.

One day Manish and his son arrived at a camp where everybody seemed to be starving. Manish said: "These people are much too thin to eat. Either we fatten them up or we leave them alone."

"Let's fatten them up, father," the son said.

So they fed the people caribou meat for one whole week. At the end of this week, Manish decided to find out whether they had gotten any fatter. He grabbed an old man and sliced open his elbow, but saw only bone there, along with a bit of gristle. He said to his son:

"Not fat enough yet."

Another time he visited a young girl and bit off a chunk of her shoulder. "Too lean," he said, and spat it out.

One morning the son went out hunting. After he'd left, Manish fell asleep. Just what the people were waiting for. They ran off to the woods where they'd cached some spears and lances.

Now Manish's son came back. "What happened to our people?" he asked.

Manish said, "They must have run away while I was asleep."

The son started beating his father for not paying better attention to their food supply. Old Manish beat him right back, saying: Next time *you* look after the food.

The two cannibals were so busy beating each other that they did not see the people come out of the woods. Nor did they seem to be aware of the spears which the people were sticking in their bodies.

At last the people got a little tired of sticking their spears in the cannibals and not getting any results. The *mistapeo* said:

"They must be keeping their hearts somewhere else. If we can find the place and destroy the hearts, we'll be able to destroy the cannibals, too."

So the *mistapeo* searched around for this place. Finally he found it at the top of an old birch tree. There were two hearts in a nest of moss. The *mistapeo* climbed up there and the moment his spear pierced one of the hearts, Manish let out a scream and fell dead to the ground.

"Why did my father die?" exclaimed the son. "I only wanted to break a few of his bones, not kill him."

He too died when the *mistapeo's* spear plunged into the nest again.

So it was that the people were rid of Manish and his son ... except in their dreams.

Katshiuas

One night a man named Katshiuas dreamed that an eagle came down out of the sky and attacked some rocks. When the eagle struck these rocks, all his claws broke. "Help me, brother," the bird said. "I need my claws to hunt."

Next morning Katshiuas woke up to find an eagle with broken claws outside his tent. "I'm old and my eyesight is bad," the eagle said, "so I mistook some rocks for a herd of caribou."

Katshiuas took his knife and sharpened the eagle's claws. Then he threw him a caribou skin, saying, "Here, catch this." The eagle caught it with his claws. "You won't have any problems from now on," Katshiuas told him.

"Thanks, brother," the eagle said. "In return for your help, I'll tell you a little secret. My wife eats human beings. And she has her eyes on you. Never, ever walk alone on a frozen lake."

Then the eagle flew away.

Several days later Katshiuas went out hunting. He came on a frozen lake which had a couple of beaver lodges on the opposite shore. Ah, he said to himself, I think I'll have some roasted beaver tail for supper.

Just as he was crossing the lake, a female eagle swooped down and grabbed him. She carried him up to the top of a very high rock where she had her nest. In the nest was a pair of young eagles gnawing on a human brisket.

"Didn't I tell you not to walk out alone on a frozen lake?" the old eagle said.

Katshiuas thought to himself: I must kill this fellow's wife if I want to get out of here alive. Since he might not appreciate that, I'll have to kill him, too. Along with their kids.

So he set fire to the nest. The eagles tried to put out the fire by fanning it with their wings, but in doing so they set themselves on fire.

"Burn, you cannibals! Burn!" exclaimed Katshiuas.

And the eagles burned right down to their skeletons—eagle skeletons, each of them, except for the female eagle. She burned down to the skeleton of a human being. Suddenly this skeleton looked over at Katshiuas, grinned and said: "You've burned up your own grandmother, boy. But that's all right. It's impossible to kill someone who's already dead."

Whereupon she flapped her arm bones and off she flew.

After that, Katshiuas was very careful around eagles.

The *Atcen* And The Woman

A man and his wife were cooking some caribou steaks when an *atcen* approached them. "Got room for a dinner guest?" the *atcen* said. He had an enormous white skull propped on his body and ribs that stuck out like tree limbs. The man threw a spear at him and then ran off to hide. In trying to get away herself, the woman fell over backwards and her dress went up above her waist. The *atcen* began feeling her to see if she was still alive. He felt her vagina, then smelled his fingers. "I was going to eat her," he said, "but she seems to be rotten." So he walked away … and walked back again. "Maybe her liver is still good," he said. As he reached down with his knife, the woman leaped up and pushed him into the fire. "I'm burning! I'm burning!" he cried. "I would have let you live," the woman said, "only you said I was rotten." And then she threw another log onto the fire. That's how the *atcen* died: he was burned up by an angry woman.

Beard-Heart

Once there lived an *atcen* named Beard-Heart who liked nothing better than to suck the juices from people's bodies. Once he sucked out these juices, he'd leave behind the husks. Which is why there used to be so many human husks propped against trees or lying on the ground in the old days.

One day Beard-Heart was chasing a man whom he wanted to turn into a husk. The man climbed up into a tree. Beard-Heart camped right below him, not knowing he was there. After a while the man had to piss and he pissed down a mighty stream on Beard-Heart.

"Damn rain tastes like piss," the *atcen* said. And he bent down to avoid getting it in his eyes. The man saw this, so he hopped down out of the tree and plunged his spear into Beard-Heart's back. Beard-Heart merely swatted at it, saying that the mosquitoes seemed to be a lot worse this year. Then he bent down his head again.

Now the man ran back to camp and related his story. The others were fearful that the *atcen* would soon make all of them into husks, so they got ready to break camp.

Suddenly a very old man stepped forward. "It's better to fight than flee," he said. Then he added: "Our friend tried to kill this Beard-Heart with a cold spear. Everyone knows a cold spear doesn't work with an *atcen*."

The younger man took this old man to where Beard-

Heart was sitting, his head still bent down. The old man heated up a spear. "Let him taste this," he said.

The other drove the spear deep into Beard-Heart. The *atcen* hissed, groaned, made a loud choking noise, and died. Then the old man cut open his chest and took out the heart. It was all covered with hair, just like a beard. It hissed and died, too.

After that, nobody ever found another human husk in the woods again.

IV. Animals

Atikwapeo

You ever hear about Atikwapeo? He was a man, but he kept dreaming he was a caribou. One day he woke up ... with antlers! He had a big white patch on his ass, too. Maybe I ought to join a herd, he told himself. So he went off and joined the Mucawaunipi herd.

After a while, this herd made him chief. He put down all the hunting laws. If people were killing too many caribou, Atikwapeo would say: "Brothers, keep away from those greedy human beings." He'd say this until the herd got big again. Then he would say: "Give yourselves to human beings, brothers. You can afford it now."

But that was long ago.

Nobody has seen Atikwapeo in many, many years.

A hunter must have mistaken him for a caribou and killed him.

The Hunter And The Geese

There was once a hunter who hadn't eaten for many days. He wandered around, nearly dead, and at last came to a lake where he saw a flock of geese. "Brothers," he said, "let's have a big party tonight." The geese thought this a fine idea and that night they all gathered at a certain clearing in the woods. The hunter told them to close their eyes ... he wanted to beat his drum. And as he beat it, the geese danced round and round the campfire. And as each bird passed him, the hunter grabbed it, twisted its neck, and killed it. Finally the leader caught on. "Brothers!" he shouted. "Our brother is killing us!" Now the few that were left opened their eyes and flew away.

The man had enough food for the winter, but he could never talk to geese again.

Metcimiu

Aboy, Metcimiu, was raised by his uncle after his parents starved to death. The uncle was always trying to find new wives for himself, so he didn't pay much attention to Metcimiu. Or when he did, he'd ask the boy to visit a certain woman and tell her what a fine husband he'd make. Once Metcimiu didn't do as he was told and his uncle beat him, saying: "I should have left you to rot with your parents."

After this beating, the boy began to dream of bears. There was nothing else, only bears. Sometimes he would even dream he was a bear himself ... and wake up with berry juice all over his chin.

One day the uncle was lying on his sleeping skins with a new wife. "I'm too lazy to hunt today, boy," he told Metcimiu, "so go out and bring me back a caribou."

By late afternoon Metcimiu had not found a caribou. He hadn't found any other game, either. If I go back emptyhanded, he thought, uncle will beat me.

All at once he noticed a bear observing him from a spruce thicket. *"Pushu tai etin,* my son?" the bear said. "Will you come and live with me?"

"I will," Metcimiu replied. For he figured life with the bear could not be any worse than life with his uncle.

The bear took him to a cave filled with dried fish and tubs of grease.

The bear said: "My own son died by a hunter's hand long ago. I've been looking for another son for quite some time now."

Some years passed. Metcimiu grew up to be a robust

young man even as his uncle grew less and less robust. Instead of dreaming about women, the uncle began dreaming about Metcimiu. His nephew always appeared as a bear in these dreams.

Meanwhile the bear was getting a little worried about the uncle. For he'd been dreaming, too. "If he comes here, my son, please don't let him take my life."

"He will have to take mine first, father," Metcimiu said.

At last the uncle managed to find his way to the cave where his nephew was living. He was a very different man from the man whom Metcimiu had left behind. Old and nearly blind now, he couldn't even see the bear hiding from him among the dried fish. "What's that over there?" he said, pointing toward the bear.

"Just an old rug I've been sleeping on," Metcimiu said.

"It must be quite warm," observed the uncle.

Poor fellow has no eyesight, thought Metcimiu. So he decided to look after him. Holding his hand, he led the old man home.

Next winter there was almost no game at all. Metcimiu and his uncle were forced to eat their snowshoe bindings and broth from boiled down caribou hooves. Finally the uncle starved to death. Metcimiu was close to starving himself when he dreamed about the bear again. In his dream, the bear seemed to be gesturing him toward some large cache of meat. But where was this meat? With his last strength, Metcimiu went to the bear's cave.

"Eat me, my son," the bear said.

"I can't do that. You're my father."

"All the more reason to eat me ..."

So Metcimiu ate his father and, in doing so, managed to survive the winter.

The First Loon

L ong ago there were two lovers, a brother and sister. All night long they would fondle and embrace on their sleeping skins. This did not please their parents, who said: You can love each other and be first cousins, but not, certainly *not,* brother and sister.

"But why can't I love my brother?" the sister asked.

"And why can't I love my sister?" asked the brother.

"Because it's unhealthy, that's why," their parents said.

Hearing this, they loved each other even more.

At last the *mistapeo* spoke out against them: "A brother and sister who are lovers, that will bring a bad winter and plenty of starving."

The boy was forced to go into hiding. But wherever he hid, near or far, he'd only need to sing and his sister would hear him. And then she would come running.

Several months passed and the girl gave birth to a baby boy. She was carrying it in her moss-bag when one of her older brothers said: "I hope a lynx bites out its heart!"

"How can you say such a nasty thing?" the girl asked.

"Because your baby is unhealthy, that's why."

The girl did not understand this at all. To her, the baby looked as healthy as any she'd ever seen.

Now the girl's brothers decided to do something about the father of this baby. Although he was their younger brother, he was bringing shame on the family.

The best way to get rid of this shame, they figured, was to get rid of the boy himself.

A while later the boy was singing for his sister. The girl put on her snowshoes and followed his song. The brothers tracked their sister all the way to the shore of Michikimau. And there, in the middle of the frozen lake, the boy was waiting.

"Look at the lovely baby I've brought you!" the girl exclaimed.

Just then one of the brothers shot an arrow directly into the baby's heart. "It's not lovely anymore," he said.

The boy knew they would try to shoot his heart, too. So he quickly sang a hole in the ice. He took off all his clothes and jumped into this hole. The next instant he was a loon, flying up out of the cold water. And as he flew, he cried mournfully, for his sweetheart would never come to him again.

Stupid Lemmings

A wolverine was lying on his back. Lemmings came from far and wide to see him. Happy is the day, they said, when one of those nasty wolverines dies. But this nasty wolverine was only playing dead. Every time one of the lemmings got near him, he'd open his mouth and swallow it.

At last the wolverine had swallowed all but two lemmings, both quite young. These lemmings cried: "Please eat us, too!"

"You're too little," said the wolverine, "but come back when you grow up and I'll be glad to eat you."

The little lemmings stood there and cried over and over again: Oh please eat us, please eat us ...

Meanwhile the wolverine went to sleep. Just what the two lemmings had been waiting for. They leaped into his mouth, slid down the throat, and scampered into his stomach. There they found all the other lemmings, including their parents.

"Mother! Father!" the little lemmings shouted.

"So good of you to join us, children," said their parents.

They celebrated being together again with a big *mukoshan* in the wolverine's stomach. All night long they danced and sang.

Next day they were shit.

Such is life, my friends.

The Origin Of Robins

A man, Aiasheu, had a wife and son. One day he noticed some scratches on his wife's breast. "Who made those scratches, woman?" he demanded.

Replied his wife: "I snared a partridge. While I was getting it out of the snare, it scratched me."

"Those look like love scratches to me. Are you sure you haven't been sleeping with our son?"

"Certainly not!"

Yet the more Aiasheu thought about this, the more he believed it. Why were his wife and son always picking berries together? What did they do when he went out hunting? Hadn't he once seen the boy fingering his mother's thigh at a *mukoshan?*

Now he was convinced that his wife and son were sleeping together. He decided to take the boy on a little trip ... a little trip from which he would not return.

Father and son paddled their canoe to an island. "There are some duck eggs on those rocks, boy," Aiasheu said. "Why don't you gather a few?"

After the boy had jumped out of the canoe and waded ashore, Aiasheu began paddling away. "I'm leaving you here," he yelled back to his son, "because you're been sleeping with your mother."

"That's not true!" the boy protested.

"Tell it to the wolves who'll be picking over your bones ..."

Back in camp Aiasheu told his wife that the boy had drowned when their canoe had flipped over. It was fortunate that he, her husband, knew how to swim or he would have drowned, too.

Now the man started treating his wife very badly. He'd throw her out of the tent, with no clothes on, in the middle of winter. Or he'd feed her lemmings, saying that if foxes could eat lemmings, so could she. Or he'd simply beat her until she felt her body would break.

Several years passed. The woman had a dream about her son. He was alive, the dream said, and soon would appear at her tent with a *tabaskan* piled high with meat. She told her husband this dream, but his only response was to beat her. "Our son is dead," he said. "His bones have turned yellow by now."

"No," the woman replied. "He is alive. I have dreamed it so. And he will bring us meat."

Now Aiasheu was so angry with his wife that he pushed her into the fire. "Taste your own meat, woman, if you're so hungry," he told her.

Just then a young man emerged from the bush with a *tabaskan*. He dropped the lead and reached into the fire, pulling out the woman. After he'd done this, he pushed in Aiasheu.

"You are my son," Aiasheu screamed. "Please don't let me burn up!"

"I don't have a father anymore," the young man said, throwing a birch log onto the fire to make it burn faster.

The woman had some very bad burns on her chest and seemed to be in pain. The young man took pity on her, saying that she didn't have to be a human being anymore. He asked what creature she would like to be. I would like to be a bird, my son, she said.

And all at once the old woman was flying up into the sky, with red feathers on her breast where she'd been burned.

That's how robins came into the world.

Mesapus

Mesapus went out hunting.
He came upon a she-bear so old she couldn't walk anymore. "Goodbye, grandmother," he said, and thrust his *shimagin* into her chest. Then he skinned her and put on her skin as if it were his own skin.

A while later the she-bear's family came back from a hunting trip. They saw Mesapus standing outside the den. "Hey!" they exclaimed. "Our grandmother can walk again!"

Mesapus said: "Someone must have been conjuring with me."

That night he slept in a corner with the young cubs. He killed one of them for his meat cache. Next morning he woke up the others: "*Tshispeu! Tshispeu!* My grandson is dead!"

Nobody suspected Mesapus of being the murderer himself. They gathered around and comforted him, saying: "Poor old dear! That little one was your favorite grandson, too."

Next night he killed another of the cubs. And the following morning he broke into the same wail: "My grandson is dead! My grandson is dead!"

Once again nobody suspected Mesapus. After all, he was their beloved old grandmother.

Now Mesapus always stayed home while the others went hunting. One day he was home, asleep, when a wolf happened to see him. It's an old she-bear, the wolf thought: She won't be very tasty, but at least she'll be an easy kill.

So the wolf pounced on Mesapus and killed him.

Moral: He who lives like a bear must expect to die like one.

Storm

Big storm coming, said Shushebish, but I'm such a great hunter that I'll just whistle in its face.

Storm arrives. Black sky all over, screeching wind. Storm bites Shushebish.

Who dares to bite a hunter like me? he shouted, waving his bow.

Storm bites him again. Again. Yet again. At last he knew: the storm was a sky-darkening cloud of mosquitoes.

Soon only Shushebish's bones were left.

Friends: Nobody is so great a hunter that there isn't a greater hunter somewhere in the world.

The Master Of Mosquitoes

A man named Pinip was such a terrible hunter that people thought some sort of curse must have been put on him. For no one could be that terrible all on his own. Sometimes Pinip would spend an entire day stalking a caribou, only to realize he'd been stalking a rock. Or he'd stalk a black spruce, thinking it was a black bear.

At last Pinip's wife got tired of an empty belly, so she took her children and went to live with her parents. After she left, Pinip stopped hunting altogether and ate only roots and berries, along with the occasional dead fish. These things he could stalk rather easily.

One day Pinip was searching for some berries when a swarm of mosquitoes attacked him. He tried to swat them away, but the more he swatted, the more they attacked. The more they attacked, the weaker he got.

At last Pinip said to the mosquitoes: "I give up. You may take my life, bloodsuckers. It's not worth much anyway."

He flung off all his clothes to make it easier for them.

Now hundreds of mosquitoes came out of the woods and settled on Pinip's body until it was little more than a mass of reddish bites.

"Good, good," Pinip said. "You're killing me."

He was on the ground, nearly dead, when he heard a voice say:

"Leave this poor man alone. Can't you see he has enough trouble already? He doesn't need us, too."

Suddenly the swarm departed. Pinip looked up and saw an enormous mosquito standing over him. "Who are you?" he asked.

"I am the Master of Mosquitoes ..."

"Why did you save my life?"

"Because that's my job. If I weren't around to watch over them, my children would kill every human being in the world."

Now the Master touched Pinip's body softly with his wing and all Pinip's bites went away. He touched him again and Pinip seemed to grow flesh on his bones. He touched him a third time and now Pinip was a mosquito himself. A big healthy mosquito with plenty of human blood in his belly.

Pinip, it's said, lived happily ever after.

Ushkeu's Anger

A man named Ushkeu, Earthworm, was always throwing out his anger. At first it would merely strike people in the face. Or knock them to the ground. Then one day his brother-in-law made fun of him because he was so thin.

"If you get any thinner, Ushkeu," the brother-in-law said, "we'll be using you to stitch our mocassins ..."

Ushkeu's anger became a raven which pecked out both the brother-in-law's eyes.

From then on, his anger always turned into some sort of animal. Once it became a beaver which gnawed a hole in his uncle's canoe, drowning the old man. Another time it turned into a bear ... and this bear tore to pieces Ushkeu's own son after the boy dropped some fat at a *mukoshan*.

People wondered how they could stop Ushkeu.

And yet they knew they couldn't get rid of a man just because he was angry all the time.

Then it happened that Ushkeu threw out his anger at a little girl who'd stepped over his snowshoe tracks.

"Don't you know that means bad luck?" Ushkeu shouted.

"It was an accident," the girl told him.

"Doesn't matter," he said. Now his anger turned into a fierce old wolf. But instead of attacking the girl, this wolf leaped onto Ushkeu himself and bit away at his neck until his head fell off.

Now Ushkeu shrank down to the size of an earthworm. He *was* an earthworm, too. And no one ever saw him again because he dug a hole in the ground and hid there.

Lightning Tricked By A Mosquito

One day Lightning was very hungry, so he asked a mosquito what sort of food it'd been eating. The mosquito didn't want to say human blood. For Lightning looked like he had an enormous appetite and might eat so much human blood that there wouldn't be any left for anyone else. So the mosquito flew over to a tree and said: "See the pitch here? That's what I've been eating." Now Lightning tried to eat this pitch himself, but he only succeeded in splitting the tree trunk. He tried again with a different tree, but he split that one, too. Poor Lightning! He's still hungry, even today, and still splitting trees.

How The Summer Birds
Were Brought North

This happened a long time ago, during a very bad winter. A little boy would not stop crying. He cried all day, all night. Cried so loud he kept the whole camp awake. Cried even when he was fed a nice roasted caribou heart by his parents.

"Tell us why you're crying, son," his parents asked him.

"I want birds," he said.

"Eating-type birds?"

"No, singing-type birds. Summer birds. That's the type of birds I want."

The boy was driving everyone crazy with his crying, so his parents went to see the *mistapeo*.

"Best thing is, get him some of these summer birds," the *mistapeo* declared. "The next best thing? Throw him in the sea and drown him ..."

The parents decided in favor of getting the birds. But where could they get summer birds in the middle of winter? It would not be easy. They called a meeting of animals: Wolf, Porcupine, Otter, Muskrat, and Fisher.

"If you'll get those summer birds for me," the boy's father announced, "I won't hunt you anymore. I'll hunt only caribou."

That sounded like a pretty good arrangement to the animals. So they got in their canoe and off they paddled, due south, with Wolf in the stern.

A while later they arrived at Master Beaver's lodge. Master Beaver cooked up three of his offspring in honor of their visit. Then he sliced off some of his own fat and likewise cooked it up, saying: "Find those birds, please. That damn kid's driving me crazy, too."

The animals set off again. After paddling for one whole moon, they came to another lodge. Here lived the old man who kept the summer birds during the winter.

"Could we borrow your birds for a while?" Wolf asked the old man.

"Sorry," the old man said, "but I can't allow that. The birds have to stay here until winter runs its course. Besides, my wife likes to hear them sing and she'd kill me if I let them go."

The old man's wife was a big ugly sucker fish. At the mention of her name she stuck her head out of the water and grinned a big ugly grin.

"Aren't you bothered by that kid's crying?" Wolf inquired.

"I am," said the old man, "but I'm not giving up those birds, long-snout."

Meanwhile Otter had floated an old tree past the lodge. It had lots of gnarled limbs, which made it look like a rack of antlers. "Ah," exclaimed the old man, "moose meat for supper!" He hopped into his canoe and paddled after the tree. Once he was gone, the animals grabbed the birchbark baskets in which the birds were imprisoned.

"Husband! Husband!" shouted the sucker fish. "They tricked you. They're getting away with our birds ..."

The old man turned around and began following the other canoe. "Come back with my birds, you thieves!" he yelled. And he started shooting arrows in their direction.

Muskrat did not want to get hit, so he jumped into

the water. The old man quickly paddled up to him and tried to drown him.

Said Muskrat: "I *live* underwater, old man. So you can't drown me there."

Then the old man started whacking at Porcupine with his paddle. The paddle came down on Porcupine's quills and stuck there. Now the old man could not paddle his canoe anymore.

"Don't worry, husband," said the sucker fish, and she began pushing the canoe. It shot through the water so fast that it rammed right into the other canoe.

"Quick, Fisher, do something," Wolf said. "I'm too busy paddling."

So Fisher jumped onto the shore. He hoped to lure the old man there, but the old man would not be lured. Instead he shot an arrow directly into Fisher's ass. So great was the pain from this arrow that Fisher leaped up, up, up into the sky and became the Fisher Star.

The old man was so astonished by this that he simply gazed up at the sky. He continued to gaze up there even as Wolf was paddling farther and farther away from him. At last Wolf was out of sight ... and the old man was still gazing up at the sky.

The animals got back home with the summer birds just in time for the arrival of summer itself. Once there, they opened the birchbark baskets and set the birds free. Whereupon the little boy grabbed his bow and killed one of the birds, took off the skin and put it on over his own skin.

For he was really a bird trapped in human form.

That's why he'd been crying.

"Is that you, son?" his father asked.

"Yes, father," the boy replied, "and I'll see you again next year."

Then off he flew to join his brothers.

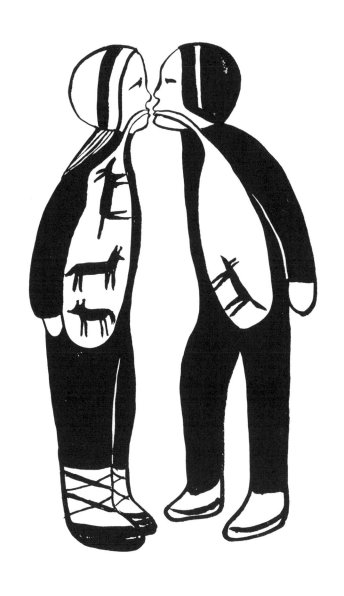

V. Magic And Taboos

The Wolf

Once upon a time a boy fell sick. When he tried to move, he felt pain. In his stomach was a howling which frightened people.

So an old *mistapeo* came to the boy's tent. Our son is dying, the mother told the man. The *mistapeo* listened to the boy's body, then he looked up and said: "This boy has swallowed a wolf."

"Swallowed a wolf?" exclaimed the father.

"Yes, and it's the wolf that's sick. The boy is fine."

"We must get the wolf out of him ..."

"No," said the *mistapeo,* "you must not. The boy will die then. Instead the wolf must be cured."

Now the old man bent down and listened again. He said: "The wolf seems to need another wolf—a female."

"Isn't one wolf in my son enough?" inquired the father.

"He needs two wolves. Otherwise, the one will always be sick."

The *mistapeo* left the tent. He was gone for quite a while. When he came back, he had a young girl with him. "She has three wolves in her," he explained. "That's one wolf too many."

Now the girl put her lips to the boy's lips. All of a

sudden there was a noise like a big animal moving from one den to another.

"Her wolf has gone to the boy," the *mistapeo* said, "which means his wolf will be all right now."

So it happened that the boy got back his health.

The Shit Man

Once a big wind struck a camp and swept all the shit together into a man. This man stood up. Stretched his limbs. And began walking around. Wherever he went, people would say: "Take your awful smell somewhere else, Shit Man."

"I'll be glad to do that," the Shit Man told them, "if you'll give me some clothes to cover my nakedness."

Right away they gave him a nice caribou-skin shirt and some leggings, moccasins with otter-fur fringes, and a beaded neck amulet.

"I'd like a canoe, too."

They gave him a freshly-sewn birchbark canoe, saying: "Here, take it, and get out of our camp."

The Shit Man took the canoe and paddled downriver until he came to another camp. A boy came out to see if he was friend or enemy. "I'll only talk to the headman," the Shit Man announced, puffing up his chest.

So the headman paddled out to his canoe. Ah, he thought to himself, this fellow must be very important, he's dressed so well. I'll bring him back and feast him, and maybe I'll get something out of it.

All at once the wind changed. The headman thought: My new friend smells bad, it's true, but if I mention this to him, he might be insulted.

Thus the Shit Man was brought ashore and a feast prepared in his honor. All the young girls gathered around him, for they thought he might make a good partner for the night. But when they smelled him, they quickly changed their minds.

In the midst of the feast, it started to rain. The Shit Man knew he would drip away in this rain, so he leaped to his feet and ran into the woods.

"It seems we've insulted our guest," the headman declared. "That's not good, not good at all, because he's so important."

And he went off in search of this guest. In a little clearing, he saw the clothes, mocassins, and neck amulet the man had been wearing, yet he couldn't seem to find the man himself. All he found was a fresh pile of shit.

The Haunted Lodge

Two hunters got caught in a bad blizzard. They took refuge in a lodge which was empty except for a bundle of furs hung from the rafters. That night the hunters were smoking their pipes.

"I will tell you a story about two men," the elder man said. "They were caught in a bad blizzard and they hadn't brought a tent with them ..."

"What happened then?"

"They found a nice little lodge in the middle of the woods ..."

"And what happened then?"

"I'm too tired to finish. I'll tell you the rest tomorrow."

Next morning the younger man went over to his friend and shook him. Wake up! he shouted. But the man did not wake up. Nor would he ever wake up, for he had died in his sleep.

Poor fellow, thought the other: my friend gave up his breath before he could finish his story. That means the story is somewhere in this lodge, waiting for an end. I'll have to stay here myself ... until I find the end.

The man looked for the end of the story all day long. Toward evening he curled up on the floor to go to sleep. He happened to glance up at the bundle of furs. Suddenly a skeleton peered out of it. "Another person for me to strangle," the skeleton said.

Now a long bony arm reached down and grabbed at the man. He rolled away from it. "Who ... who are you?" he asked.

Came this reply: "I starved in this lodge long ago. Since then I've killed everyone who comes here. I killed your friend last night. Tonight I'm going to kill you."

"Isn't that rather cruel"

"Perhaps, but life is supposed to be cruel ..."

How can I escape this murderous skeleton? the man asked himself even as the bony arm made another lunge for his throat.

All at once he remembered his friend's unfinished story. It was still here, still in the lodge. So the man jumped into the story and that's exactly how it ended— he escaped the skeleton.

Do Not Kill A Dream

A man dreamed of a good salmon fishing place by a river. He went there, sat down on the bank, and fished for one whole moon. All he caught was a cold in his chest. I'll kill that dream, he said. So he fell asleep grasping his knife. The dream told him of another good fishing place. The man thrust his knife, thrust it again. The dream let out a sigh and died. Now the man did not even know where the bad fishing places were and he died, too.

The Origin Of Spruce Sap

Once two sisters had a camp to themselves. The younger girl was named Pitsu. Each could hunt, fish, and trap on her own, without help from a man.

One evening a man happened to visit their camp. He had nowhere to sleep, he said, and asked if he could sleep in their tent. It was quite cold outside, so neither Pitsu nor her sister had any objection to this.

The man slept right beside Pitsu. In the middle of the night, he placed his hand between her legs. She did not push it away.

"Do you like that?" he asked.

"Yes," she said, "but I don't know what it means."

"It means you're supposed to get excited."

Said Pitsu: "I only get excited when I see the northern lights children dancing across the sky."

This girl is really innocent, the man thought, but I know how to change that ... He cut off one of his testicles and stuck it in Pitsu's vagina. Since he was a *mistapeo,* he could conjure up another one, no problem, whenever he wished.

"Why did you do that?" asked Pitsu.

"I did it to make you interested in men. Keep it there and you'll soon notice the difference. Maybe one day I'll come back and claim you."

Next morning the man left. Pitsu was eager to see what would happen when another man showed up. A couple of days later a pair of hunters, father and son, arrived at the camp and asked if they could spend the night. Be our guests, the elder sister told him. The father slept next to her while the son slept next to Pitsu.

The man right next to her made Pitsu very excited. In the middle of the night, she reached over and grabbed his hand and put it between her legs.

"Hey, woman!" the man exclaimed, feeling the testicle. "What's that you've got down there?"

"I borrowed it from a friend," Pitsu said.

The man was so upset by this that he woke his father and both decided to spend the night elsewhere.

Several days later another hunter, young and good-looking, came to the camp. It wasn't cold, but Pitsu asked him to stay the night anyway. As was her custom, she took his hand and put it between her legs.

"You seem to have grown a testicle, woman" the hunter said.

"What's a testicle?" asked Pitsu.

"Something only a man should have," he told her. And then he ran off into the night, too.

Poor Pitsu! Every time a man came to camp, she somehow managed to frighten him away. She thought to herself: If I can't have a man, maybe I can have a woman. So she asked her sister to sleep with her.

The sister had no objection to this. Indeed, she said she'd always wanted to lie down and fondle Pitsu's loins.

Soon the girls had pulled off each other's leggings.

The sister saw Pitsu's testicle.

"You shouldn't have *that* between your legs, dear Pitsu," she said. And she yanked out the testicle and flung it WHACK! against a spruce tree. It split right open and all the juices flowed down along the bark of the tree.

And that's how spruce sap came into the world.

Pitsu, it's said, never had an interest in men again.

Tcibas

A young man named Tcibas owned a pair of peculiar leggings. He'd want to walk in one direction, they'd want him to walk in another. Usually, the leggings won. And then Tcibas would end up going somewhere he had no wish to go, like his neighbor's shitpile.

Get rid of those leggings, people told him.

If I can't master a pair of leggings, Tcibas would reply, I'm not much of a man. I wouldn't be much of a woman, either.

So he kept the leggings. One day they led him to a high cliff.

But I didn't want to come here, Tcibas said. I just wanted to go fishing ...

And then the leggings jumped off the cliff.

Tcibas' body was broken up on the rocks below. All because he'd killed his father and taken the old man's caribou-skin leggings for himself.

The Man Who Used His Son For Bait

Each day a man would go out with his fishing line, but he never seemed able to catch any fish. Perhaps I'm using the wrong type of bait, he said to himself. So he decided to put his young son at the end of his fishing line.

"Isn't there some sort of taboo against that?" the man's wife said to him.

"Maybe," replied the man, "but I don't care as long as I catch some fish."

Now he made a hole in the ice and flung his son in the water.

He waited all day for a bite.

Toward evening he felt a big tug on his line. But when he lifted it up, the hook was gone ... along with his son.

His wife said, "I told you not to use our son for bait."

"Don't worry, woman," the man said. "I'll get him back."

Now he leaped into the water himself. As he swam down to the bottom, he passed the camps of many fish, but in none of these camps did he see his son. At last he noticed a very large camp set back among the weeds. And there, all tied up, was his son.

"I'm so glad you're here, father," the boy said. "They're planning a *mukoshan* and I'm the food."

"Not if I can help it ..."

Whereupon the man grabbed his son and started swimming toward the surface. When the fish saw this, they swam after him, yelling: "Come back with our food, you thief!"

Now the man swam up to the hole and climbed out onto the ice. The fish were swimming after him so fast that they flew right out of the water and landed on the ice themselves. One by one, the man clubbed them to death.

That's how he ended up catching some fish.

Napao

An old man, Napao, dreamed of huge teeth gnawing at his lungs. Stop your gnawing! he cried, but the teeth gnawed on. GET AWAY FROM MY LUNGS! he cried, still louder. People came to see why Napao was making so much noise. They saw beaver tracks walking into his sleep. Quick, they said, shake loose the beaver. They shook and shook, but the beaver held on. Stop gnawing at my lungs! Napao cried one last time. Then he gave up his breath. Whereupon the beaver left his sleep.

A Head Of Lice

A boy had so many lice that his scratching kept his parents awake at night. At last they decided to leave him behind ... else they would never get any sleep. So one morning they packed up their gear. That's nice, thought the boy, we're going on a trip. He asked his mother to help him put on his snowshoes.

"Only when we're finished packing our skins," she told him. But after they finished, she hauled the *tabaskan* onto the soft snow and off she went with her husband.

"Wait for me! Wait for me!" the boy cried.

"You have too many lice for us," his parents called back.

The boy ran after them, but he was barefoot and his feet began to freeze. Now I'll die, he thought: At least I hope I'll die.

Just then a very tall man emerged from the woods. When the boy saw this man, he shouted: "Mother! There's a giant come to eat me."

"You don't want your mother, boy," the giant said. "It's because of her that you're unhappy."

"Who are you?"

"Your old grandfather. Death has changed my shape somewhat. I'm a lot taller than when I was alive. Also, stronger."

Now the giant bent down and began picking the lice from the boy's head. He picked off all but two, saying that if he picked off these two, a male and a female, there wouldn't be any lice in the world. And lice, he declared, have their place, too.

Then the giant lifted up the boy and carried him to his parents' camp. "Who brought you here?" his mother demanded.

The boy pointed to the giant. His mother screamed: "It's a monster!"

"You're the monster, woman," the giant said, "for you left your son behind to die. From now on, I'll be living with you to make sure it doesn't happen again."

So it was that the giant lived right there in the tent with the family. Each night he'd blow on the boy to make him grow. At last the boy had grown so big that he could go out hunting alone.

One day the boy came back to the tent only to discover that the giant had left. He followed the giant's tracks, yelling: "Grandfather! Grandfather!" When the giant heard these words, he stopped. The boy caught up with him.

"You said you'd stay with me," the boy said.

"That's true," the giant replied, "but you don't need me anymore. See how big you've grown? You're almost a man now."

Now the giant picked up the boy and blew on him one last time. With this breath, the boy flew through the air all the way back to camp. Upon landing, he said to his parents:

"If anyone's going to leave anyone else behind, dear parents, it's *I* who'll be leaving *you* behind ..."

After that, there were no more complaints about lice. Indeed, the boy's mother often pleaded with him to let her pick off his two remaining lice. But he refused to allow this. For lice, he said, have their place, too.

Why Some People Starved Near Indian House Lake

Many years ago near Indian House Lake, some people caught a whiskey jack and plucked off all its feathers. Look at the silly bird! they laughed. The whiskey jack flapped its wings and flew ... nowhere. Yet it kept flapping away. At last it flapped so much that it made a very big wind. With this wind came a storm. Snow covered the tops of trees. The people were stuck in their tents and lo! they starved to death. All because they'd abused a poor fellow creature.

Sheshin

A man, Sheshin, killed a bear and did not offer it tobacco. That bear will not be happy, Sheshin's wife said. Sheshin laughed: How can a dead bear be happy anyway?

Meanwhile the dead bear told his fellow bears not to give themselves to Sheshin.

That's why he never killed another bear again.

And the bear also told the caribou and beavers not to give themselves to him.

That's why he didn't kill another caribou or beaver, either.

So it was that he became known as Apukushish Sheshin, Mouse Sheshin, because he killed only mice.

Kakwa's Wife

A hunter named Kakwa had a wife who was always complaining. If he brought home a caribou, she'd say it had worms. If he brought back a rabbit, it'd be too thin. Or if it was a porcupine, too prickly. And what's that bad smell, Kakwa dear? Have you been bathing in beaver piss again?

At last Kakwa paid a visit to the local *mistapeo*. "Kill my wife," he said, "and I'll give you a beaded shot pouch."

"Killing people is wrong," the *mistapeo* told him. "On the other hand, it's not wrong to change their shapes a little. Just leave it to me."

Kakwa got back home to find that his wife had turned into ... a skinning knife!

Maybe she'll stop nagging me now, he thought.

And Kakwa's wife did stop nagging him, too. From then on, she skinned all his game and never an unkind word from her mouth. Kakwa, for his part, kept her in a nice leather sheath so that no harm would come to her. It is said that they had a quite happy life together.

Where Thunder Comes From

Long ago no one knew where thunder came from. Maybe clouds did it, maybe the stars. Maybe the moon did it, maybe the sun. Maybe Tciwetinowinu himself did it, after eating a bad piece of meat.

One day a *mistapeo* shot an arrow into the sky and an enormous goose fell from the mists. This goose honked so loudly upon approaching the earth that human beings had to cover their ears or they'd burst. It fell into a lake and made this lake so hot that all the fish burned up. Thought the *mistapeo:* It seems I've done a bad thing. So he pulled the arrow from the goose, whereupon the bird made a loud BOOM! and returned to its home in the sky.

Since then, nobody has tried to bring down thunder again.

The Little Man

A man lived in a caribou's ass. He could live there quite easily because he was a very little man ... so little that the caribou did not even know he was there.

One day the little man fell out of his host's ass and landed on the ground SPLAT! with a pile of his host's droppings.

A young girl saw him emerge like that. "What sort of person lives in a caribou's ass?" she laughed.

"What sort of person doesn't?" the little man said.

The girl thought this a rather cute reply, so she picked him up and brought him back to camp with her. She showed him to all her friends, saying: "Look what I found! He came right out of a caribou's ass!"

It wasn't long before the girl was treating the little man as if he were her child. She'd cradle him in her arms, even put him against her breast. When she went somewhere, she'd stick him in a moss-bag and carry him on her back ... except when she went to take a piss.

One morning the girl walked into the woods to take a piss. The little man followed her. When she'd finished, he went to where she'd pissed and pissed there himself.

Several months later the girl's father saw she was pregnant. "You'll have to marry the man," he told her.

"I'll marry no man. Because no man has done this to me. I sleep alone."

A little while later the girl gave birth to a baby boy. Once again she insisted the baby had no father. Her own father asked the *mistapeo* if such a thing was possible.

"Only if someone has been conjuring with her," the *mistapeo* said, adding: "But I'm the only one around here who knows how to conjure and it wasn't me, I promise you."

"Then how will we find the father?"

"Very simple. We'll arrange all the men in camp in a circle. The baby will be passed from man to man. When it gets to its father, it'll piss all over him."

And so all the men were brought together in a circle. The baby was passed from one to another. All at once someone shouted: "Look! It pissed on me! It pissed on me!"

But the piss turned out to be only spittle. It came from a very old man who wanted this pretty young woman to be his wife, so he'd spat all over his hands.

At last the baby had gone around the circle and it still hadn't pissed. How very strange, thought the *mistapeo*. He wondered if something was wrong with the baby's bladder. Then he happened to see the little man sitting off by himself. "Here," he said, handing him the baby, "it's your turn now."

The baby pissed all over the little man.

"That's the father," said the *mistapeo*.

But how could he be the father? everyone asked. His penis is no thicker than a bone awl. Then the little man confessed: I used my piss, not my penis, to make her pregnant. It works every time.

The girl was not pleased by this turn of events. "The man's good-looking and all that," she said, "but he's just too small. I could never marry a man that small. He'd always be getting underfoot ..."

"Nevertheless," said her father, "you'll have to marry him."

"He's *too small.*"

Now the little man spoke. "I think I have a solution to this. You see, I'm a *mistapeo* myself. A while back, I mixed my piss with the piss of my brother's wife. She became pregnant. Since my brother is also a *mistapeo,* he conjured me down to this size and stuck me in a caribou's ass."

"So what's your solution?" the girl's father asked.

"A shaking tent."

So it was that the little man ordered a tent of beaverskin to be put up and a ring of heated stones placed inside it. After this was done, he led the girl into the tent. "Hug your knees," he told her. She hugged them. Then he began beating his drum with the femur bone of a bear. At one point he turned to the girl and said:

"What would you like, my dear?"

"I'd like us to be the same size," she replied.

All of a sudden the tent started to shake. It shook and shook, as if a powerful wind was caught inside it. Then all the shaking stopped. The drumbeats stopped, too. And out of the tent the man walked, leading the girl by the hand.

The two of them were indeed the same size now. *Both* were small enough to fit inside a caribou's ass. So they got married and that's exactly where they went to live: in a caribou's ass.

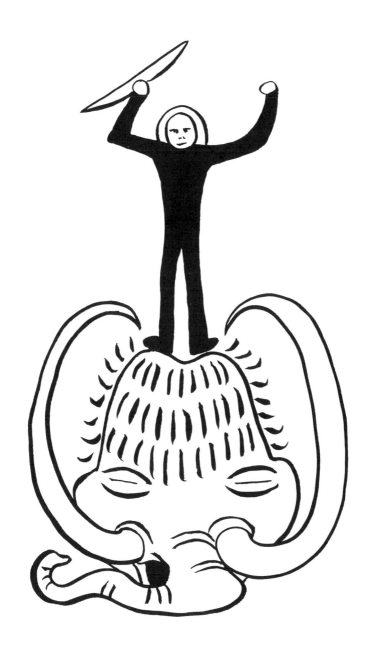

VI. TCHAKAPESH

The Birth Of Tchakapesh

Once upon a time a man and his wife were chopping down trees for firewood. They were making so much noise at this that they woke up Mammoth.

"What creature is disturbing my sleep?" roared Mammoth. He found the man and crushed him into the ground like a dry piece of wood. Then he ate him. The woman was pregnant and Mammoth ripped open her womb and with his tusk flung away a little boy-child. He ate the woman, too.

The couple had a daughter whom they'd left behind to tend camp. This daughter wondered why her parents were so late in getting back, so she put on her snowshoes and went out to look for them. She found the little boy-child.

"Who are you?" she said.

"I'm your brother Tchakapesh."

"I didn't know I had a brother."

"Well, I arrived a little early ..."

Now the girl picked up the boy and put him in a kettle to keep him warm. She fed him rich suet for three days and in those three days he grew to manhood. He stepped from the kettle and told his sister:

"I'm going to kill Mammoth because he killed our father and mother. I'm going to do it right now."

Tchakapesh made a bow from the rib of a caribou. But when he bent it back, it broke. Then he made a bow from the thigh-bone of a bear, but it broke, too. At last he cut down a big birch tree and bent it back and forth until he was certain it was strong enough. A whole grove of spruce trees became his arrows.

His sister said, "You can't fight Mammoth naked, brother."

"Mammoth is naked, so I'll be naked, too."

Tchakapesh walked to where Mammoth had killed his parents. He stood inside one of Mammoth's footprints and called for his brother Wolf. He said to Wolf, "Go find Mammoth for me."

"And what shall I say you want with him?"

"Just say I want to kill him ..."

Wolf's message made Mammoth very angry. He could imagine being killed by Bear and maybe even Wolf himself, but not by a puny human being. So he rumbled through the woods until he found Tchakapesh standing in the footprint.

"I thought you'd be bigger," Tchakapesh told him, "but you're little more than a slightly overgrown muskrat."

Mammoth rushed toward him, shaking the ground so violently that Tchakapesh dropped his bow. Then Mammoth picked him up and flung him against a tree. Picked him up a second time and flung him against another tree. Picked him up a third time and flung him right next to where Tchakapesh had dropped his bow.

"Before you die," Mammoth said, "I wish you'd tell me this: how can you breathe through that tiny thing between your legs?"

Tchakapesh sent an arrow into Mammoth's trunk.

"How can you breathe through *your* thing with that arrow there?" he said.

This made Mammoth even more angry. He made a lunge toward Tchakapesh with his tusks, but Tchakapesh was quicker and he sent an arrow directly into Mammoth's heart.

Mammoth toppled to the ground. He said: "You have killed me, Tchakapesh. What are you going to do with my body?"

"I'll make your ears into a mattress. Your tail will guy down my tent. As for your ribs, they'll paddle my canoe."

"That's fine. Just don't let grease from my head fall on a woman's hands. Else there'll be trouble ..."

Now Tchakapesh took his knife and started to cut up Mammoth. But no sooner would he cut off a piece of meat than it'd sprout wings and fly away.

I guess I wasn't meant to eat Mammoth, only use him, remarked Tchakapesh to himself.

In Mammoth's stomach, he found chunks of human beings. He happened to breathe on these chunks and they joined together. And started wobbling around.

Said Tchakapesh: "It seems I have the gift of *men-tociwim*. I can bring the dead back to life. But if I go around doing that, there'd be too many people and not enough game."

Whereupon he took a couple of his arrows and shot these people. They stopped wobbling.

After he cut off Mammoth's head, Tchakapesh was so tired that he curled up in the snow and went to sleep. His sister came along and saw the head lying there. Is it dead? she wondered. To find out, she touched it. The instant she got grease on her hands, the head came alive and started hopping along the ground toward Tchakapesh.

Just before the head reached him, Tchakapesh woke up and shot it with another arrow.

"We're safe from Mammoth now," he told his sister, "assuming you can keep your hands off his head."

"Don't worry," she said. But as she bent down to help him take out the arrow, she happened to touch the head again. And once again it came alive. Once again Tchakapesh had to kill it, this time with an arrow right between the eyes.

Now he buried the head deep in the ground and put a big rock on top of it. He chanted words telling it to stay down there forever. He made certain prayers.

"That, I hope, will be the last of Mammoth," said Tchakapesh.

And it was the last of Mammoth too.

Or so the old people used to say.

How Tchakapesh Got Rid
Of Some Giants

The young Tchakapesh dreamed of a hunting place by a lake, so he took his bow and went there. Upon arriving he saw a family of giants standing next to a large beaver lodge. One of the giants would reach into the lodge, pull out a beaver, and eat it, skin and all. Tchakapesh walked right up to them and grabbed a beaver for himself.

"Who are you, little man?" the giants said.

"I'm Tchakapesh. The famous hero."

"Well, you're not famous to us. What's more, you've stolen our beaver. Give it back."

"All right," said Tchakapesh. He swung the beaver around his head and whacked each of the giants with it.

The giants were not happy to be whacked in this fashion. They attacked Tchakapesh. *Tear out his liver! Squeeze his skull!* they shouted.

Now Tchakapesh took a deep breath and turned himself into an eagle. He flew away with the beaver dangling from his beak. Back in camp he became Tchakapesh again.

"Where did you get that beaver?" his sister asked.

He told her. "Now those giants will come and kill us," she cried.

"Let them."

"You didn't take away the *pustnawat.* They'll lead the giants to our camp."

"It doesn't matter," Tchakapesh yawned. And went to sleep.

A while later there came a loud rumbling from the woods. "Tchakapesh!" cried his sister. "The giants are coming!"

The giants rumbled into camp. They sported knives made from human bone. *"Gaskamu atomua!"* they shouted. "You eat dog, Tchakapesh!"

Now Tchakapesh took another deep breath and this time turned himself into a big boulder. Then he proceeded to bounce up and hit each of the giants again and again until they'd all fallen to the ground.

"Well, I guess they won't be killing any more beavers for a while," Tchakapesh told his sister.

Then he tried to turn himself back into Tchakapesh. He was still a boulder. When he went to sleep that night, he was a boulder and next morning he was a boulder, too. If I ever get out of this boulder, Tchakapesh thought, I'll stick to being myself. It's far too much trouble being something else. Also, I might get stuck in the wrong shape for the rest of my life.

All of a sudden a little woodpecker flew down from a nearby tree. "You need help, brother?" it inquired.

"I'm stuck inside this boulder," Tchakapesh said.

So the woodpecker began tapping away at the boulder. It tapped and tapped until the boulder cracked and then broke open. Out stepped Tchakapesh. "Thanks, little friend, for setting me free," he said. "Is there some way I can reward you?"

"Yes," said the woodpecker. "Never become a boulder again. If you only knew how much it hurts my beak to break them open ..."

And so it was that Tchakapesh stuck to being Tchakapesh from then on.

Tchakapesh Gets Married

There was once an old woman who scraped caribou skins all day, every day. This old woman, Mamiteueskueu, had no taste whatsoever for caribou meat. The only meat she had a taste for was the meat of young men. She'd send out her daughters to lure these young men to her camp. Then she'd crack their heads between a pair of large stones. And then she'd eat them raw.

One day Tchakapesh happened to hear the old woman's daughters laughing in the woods. "Who are those girls?" he asked his sister.

"The daughters of Mamiteueskueu. They're not so bad, but watch out for their mother. She's a terror."

That was all the invitation Tchakapesh needed. He followed the two girls back to their camp. Beside the campfire sat old Mamiteueskueu, scraping at her skins. She seemed quite pleased to see him. "Would you like a piece of caribou haunch, young man?" she asked him.

"I would, but only if you join me."

"I can't do that. You see, I only eat myself." So saying, Mamiteueskueu hacked off a piece of her own thigh and stuck it in her mouth.

"I bet that would taste better cooked," Tchakapesh said.

Suddenly the old woman grabbed her stones and tried to crack his head with them. But he ducked and she cracked only air.

"Try again, grandmother," said Tchakapesh.

She tried again, and again cracked only air.

"Now it's my turn," Tchakapesh said. He picked up the stones himself and brought them together WHACK! against her head. But her head was so big that he couldn't crack it. So he plunged a roasting stick right through her ass and set her over the fire.

"I'm burning up!" the old woman cried.

"Now you know what cooked meat is like," Tchakapesh told her.

When Mamiteueskueu was dead, her daughters jumped up and down and clapped their hands.

"You don't hate me for killing your mother?" Tchakapesh asked them.

"Oh no," they said. "We never cared for her anyway. She was always eating our boyfriends."

Now the girls could do whatever they chose. And what they chose to do, both of them, was marry Tchakapesh for one entire winter.

Tchakapesh And The Crow

O ne night Tchakapesh was poking away at a fire, trying to get the right glow of embers for his caribou steaks. But it was late and he was getting quite tired. Suddenly a crow flew down to his camp. "Mind if I join you?" the crow asked.

"Be my guest," Tchakapesh said, "only please tend this fire while I get a little sleep."

With that, Tchakapesh nodded off. The crow kneeled down and fanned his wings back and forth, back and forth, over the embers. The more he fanned, the more these embers seemed to die. Tchakapesh will kill me, he thought, if I let his fire go out.

So he fanned the embers even more vigorously. At last the fire was nothing more than a pile of cold charcoal. The crow fanned this charcoal for such a long time that he got black dust all over his body, which up to then had been completely white.

When Tchakapesh woke up, his fire was cold. There was the old crow kneeling next to it, covered with charcoal dust. "You can't be trusted, can you?" he remarked.

"Not with fires, apparently," the crow replied.

"Well, if you can't be trusted with fires, what can you be trusted with?"

"Raw meat?" ventured the crow.

"All right, friend," said Tchakapesh. "From now on, you'll be eating only raw meat. *Very* raw meat. Carrion, in fact. Not only that, but your color will always be the same as it is now."

So that's why crows are black.

Because long ago one crow spoiled a fire.

Why Salmon Are Always Swimming Up Falls

One winter Tchakapesh took Salmon's daughter to be his wife. This did not please Salmon. He wanted the girl for himself because she was quite handy around his camp. So he invited Tchakapesh to go on a little trip with him.

"What sort of trip?" Tchakapesh asked.

"I know a hunting place three days from here," Salmon said. "There you will find so many caribou that you won't need to hunt again until spring."

So they set out on this trip.

The first night Tchakapesh put his clothes to dry before the fire. Salmon rolled his into a bundle and placed this bundle under his head. In the middle of the night, he got up and threw Tchakapesh's clothes into the fire. He thought to himself: Now Tchakapesh will freeze to death, poor fellow.

Nest morning Tchakapesh put on Salmon's clothes.

"Hey! Those are mine!"

"No, they're mine," said Tchakapesh. Whereupon he used his *mentociwim* to change Salmon's clothes—mostly a bunch of old scales—into his own.

"But I'll freeze to death," Salmon said.

"Poor fellow!"

The second night they camped by a river and Salmon challenged Tchakapesh to a swimming contest. The river had a big waterfall. The one who swam to the top of this waterfall would win the contest. Thought Salmon: Tchakapesh will drown in the falls and then I'll have my daughter to myself.

Tchakapesh accepted the challenge. Both of them jumped into the river. Tchakapesh swam up the falls easily, swam back, and swam up the falls again. Salmon, however, was so tired from fighting off the cold that he couldn't make it. He tried again. Failed again.

Said Tchakapesh: "Keep at it, friend. If you try hard enough, you'll succeed. As for myself, I'm going back to my wife ..."

And so Salmon continued in his attempts to get up the falls. Each time he tried, he was thrown back on the rocks. But this did not stop him. Quite the contrary. He tried again and again to get up the falls. Indeed, he's still trying even today to get up those blasted falls.

Why Ice Cracks In The Winter

One day Tchakapesh went fishing in giant country. A giant came up to him and said: "What's that string for?"

"I am going to catch some trout," Tchakapesh replied.

The giant was very curious about this. He could catch human beings without much difficulty, but he'd never been able to catch a trout. They walked together to where Tchakapesh cut a hole in the ice.

"I'd like to catch some trout, too," the giant said.

"You want to catch them and eat them?"

"No, I want to catch them so I can break every bone in their bodies. That's how I have my fun."

"All right," said Tchakapesh, "then you must do as I tell you or you won't catch a single trout."

He handed the giant a fishing line and told him to kneel down with the line in the water. The giant thought this rather silly, but he did it anyway.

"Had a bite yet?" Tchakapesh asked.

"Not yet."

"Don't worry. You will."

Now Tchakapesh crept behind the giant and pushed him into the hole. The giant tried to climb out, but Tchakapesh kept stepping on his fingers. "I'll break every bone in your body when I get out of here," the giant told him.

That night the hole froze over ... with the giant stuck under it. He kicked and pounded at the ice. *Tchakapesh,* he cried, *you're a wad of wiping moss! I'll clean the dirt from my backside with you!* But hard as he pounded, he still could not get out.

My child: When you hear the ice cracking in the winter, that's the old giant himself. He's still down there, still trying to get out. And if he does get out, he'll come visit you, my dear sweet little child, and break every bone in your body.

The Departure Of Tchakapesh:
A Conversation

You see Tchakapesh up there?"

"Up where, *tshinish?*"

"Up in the moon, of course. After he killed all those giants, he became Man in the Moon. His sister is up there, too. Or so my grandfather told me, back fifty years ago and more."

"Tell me how Tchakapesh got to the moon, *tshinish.*"

"Well, he breathed on an arrow. He took one of his birch arrows and breathed on it *hard.* The arrow grew big, like a tree, Then he climbed up this arrow. Breathed on it again, climbed again, until he got to the moon."

"Any trouble along the way?"

"*Ehe!* Lots of trouble. The sun burned his back, his sister's back, too. That wasn't any fun. Also, his sister had a baby right when they were climbing the arrow. Tchakapesh killed it."

"Who made this baby?"

"I think it was from Tchakapesh himself. You see, he loved his sister so much, he just—made love to her! That's why he killed the baby. Because brothers aren't supposed to do that to their sisters."

"You said the sun was giving them trouble?"

"The sun was very hot. Finally Tchakapesh had to catch it with a snare. Only when the sun promised not

to burn their backs anymore did he set it free. A little
mouse untied the snare. Some say a shrew."

"From what you've been telling me, Tchakapesh
must have been more powerful—much more powerful—than the sun."

"He was like that Man there." (Points to a picture of
Jesus on the wall.)

"Let's get back to the moon. Why did he choose the
moon as his new home?"

"He knew he wouldn't starve there. He knew there'd
be plenty of game ... plenty of caribou."

"The American astronauts went to the moon, too.
Neil Armstrong and his crew."

"I heard that. But I don't think they were ever on the
moon. I think they were up in Ungava Bay, north of
here, or some place like that. Not ... not the moon.
That's Tchakapesh's place."

"You believe these old stories, *tshinish?*"

"No, I don't believe them. But they're true anyway."

GLOSSARY

apcinic—childknapping dwarf

atcen—a cannibal of monstrous shape and near-supernatural powers

atik (s.), *atikut* (pl.)—caribou

atnukan—old story; legend

catstinuisk—charm made from a bear tongue

Inueimun—the language of the Innu

ishkue—woman friend; lover

katcitouhuskw—mammoth

kentopwam—a hunting dream

Kwakwadjec—Wolverine in his mythological guise

kwoshapatcigan—shaking tent ceremony

matweun—vagina

mauats—no; never

mentociwim—magical power

mistapeo—shaman

mukoshan—feast of fat and bone marrow

Mushuauinnut—inhabitants of Utshimassits

niwegana—dried caribou meat

Ntesinan—the Labrador Peninsula

Nucimiwinnut—inhabitants of Sheshashui

piskutsikuh—scraper

pitsu—spruce sap

pushu—hello

pustnawat—sticks used as trail markers

pwam—dream

shakueikan—flensing knife

shimagin—caribou spear

shitsimeo—mosquito

tabaskan—sled

Tchakapesh—mythological hero of the Innu

Tciwetinowinu—Man of the North; weather deity

tshinish—old man

tshispeu!—alas!

utcima—white man

utligan—caribou scapula

Utshimassits—Davis Inlet

utshisk—muskrat

wapistan—marten

NOTES ON THE TALES

I. WOLVERINE THE TRICKSTER

Wolverine Creates the World. Told by Apinam Ashini, Sheshashui, this tale exists in many versions among Algonquin-speaking peoples. More polite versions describe
Wolverine (or his equivalent) taking the ground from
Muskrat's armpit or from out of his paws.

As Creator, glutton, dupe, shaman, lecher, braggart,
and all-purpose trickster, Wolverine is the most engag-
ing figure in Innu lore. Yet the wolverine itself, the
most ill-tempered, smelliest (I do not exclude the
skunk) of all the mustelids, is considerably less engag-
ing in real life. A single wolverine can be the ruination
of a trapline or a hunter's camp. "They thumb their
noses at us," an Innu man told me, not without admiration. Wolverines also seem to be thumbing their noses
at Nature: they're the only northern mammal whose
fur actually turns darker, instead of lighter, in the
winter. Such, perhaps, is a trickster's prerogative.

Why Certain Creatures Live in Rotten Tree Stumps. Collected from Gilbert Rich, Utshimassits, shortly before
his death in 1989. Here and elsewhere Wolverine's
carnal antics are similar to those of Coyote or, as he's
known among the Hopi, *lowason'isaw* ("cunt-craving
Coyote"). The allusion to Wolverine's blanket also re-
calls Episode 13 of the Wenebojo trickster cycle of the
Ojibwa: Trickster locates the whereabouts of his blanket only by coaxing his penis into limpness.

Tciwetinowinu. Known as The Man of the North,
Tciwetinowinu is the figure whom the Innu associate

with lousy weather. Out of deference to him, a man will always pitch his tent so that the opening faces due south ... else Tciwetinowinu might get angry and blast that tent with, well, typical Labrador weather.

The Giant Skunk. The skunk is not native to Labrador, but neither is the teller of this tale, Philip Michel. Half a century ago he trekked overland to Sheshashui from Sept-Iles, Quebec. Sept-Iles abounds with skunks.

Why Shrews Are Shrews. The shrew in question is presumably the pygmy shrew Microsorex hoyi), the only shrew in Labrador. As North America's smallest mammal, the pygmy shrew seldom weighs more than $\frac{1}{12}$ of an ounce. If you felt so inclined, you could stick one in an envelope and mail it from Boston to Los Angeles for the minimum postal rate.

How Wolverine Got Stuck in a Bear's Skull. Collected from John Poker, Tshinish Pasteen, and Thomas Pastitshi, Utshimassits.

Wolverine Eats His Own Ass. From Apinam Ashini, Sheshashui. I'd like to commend this little tale to anyone who thinks that William S. Burroughs, in *Naked Lunch,* originated the talking ass story, Wolverine's ass talks again in another tale, of which I heard only a fragment: it complains about not getting enough food, so Wolverine slips it a piece of bear meat—or I should say slips himself a piece of bear meat *per anum.*

Wolverine mistakes his scabs for *niwegana*—dried caribou meat mixed with fat and marrow.

How Wolverine Tried to Destroy the World. From a conversation with Apinam Ashini, Sheshashui. Labrador Indians always cook their meat whereas their neighbors to the North, the Inuit, do not. Indeed, "Eskimo" may derive from an archaic, more or less pejorative Inueimun word, *wuaskimowok,* meaning "eaters of raw meat."

Amusk. Variants heard in both Utshimassits and Sheshashui.

A Woman and Her Dog. Gilbert Rich, Utshimassits. Certain parts of a bear used to be considered "man's food"; a woman who deigned to eat a bear's heart or head, for instance, humiliated the dead animal's spirit irreparably.

Niassa. The leech is doubtless the large black leech of northern waters, called *akaki* by the Innu.

Every animal and even some non-animals have masters whom human beings must respect. According to Thomas Pastitshi, who told this tale, even farts have a master. Known as Mitshikapeu, the Master of Farts controls all aspects of flatulence, including time, place, and situation.

The Lemming and the Shit. Heard at a home-brew party in Sheshashui.

Puan Takes a Lover. With its intimations of the Garden of Eden myth, this story, told by Uinipapeu Rich (Utshimassits), is probably of post-contact vintage. There are no snakes in Labrador except the metaphorical variety first introduced by the Jesuits in the 17th century.

Utshisk Lake. Utshisk is Inueimun for muskrat.

The Wolf Girl and the Otter. A large aorta in the caribou's heart has a series of valves which resemble otter tracks. These valves are the inspiration behind this story, according to its teller, Gilbert Rich (Utshimassits).

The Penis. Heard from Uinipapeu Rich, Utshimassits. In former days, an Innu woman would be obliged to pull her husband's sled. This tale suggests how she might have felt about that. Along with "The *Atcen* and the Woman" (q.v.), it was characterized by Uinipapeu as "a

145

woman's story." Traditionally, a man would no more tell a woman's story than put on women's clothing.

III. Cannibals

The Cannibal Lynx. Heard from Gilbert Rich, Utshimassits. Different versions of this tale feature different anthropophagi, including one version where a Protestant missionary (!) eats himself.

"Give Me Back My Father." The cannibalistic *atcen* is the Innu equivalent of the Cree/Ojibwa/Salteaux windigo. *Atcens* possess a highly idiosyncratic form of eyesight: they see animals as people (inedible) and people as animals (edible). They're usually described as being very tall, having white hair and white skin, with protruding, owl-like eyes and a bad smell. More often than not, they're constructed of ice. *Atcens* are thought to be otherwise ordinary people who, in partaking of human flesh, have become supernaturally endowed. A man who narrated several *atcen* stories, Luke Nui (Sheshashui), told me that he'd never seen an *atcen*, but he knew a priest in Quebec who killed one some years ago by brandishing a Bible at it.

The Mistapeo Who Became a Skeleton. This story, told by the late Matthew Rich (Sheshashui), contains an almost classic description of the *vagina dentata* phenomenon, wherein the female sexual orifice bites off the male member.

The Son-in-Law's Revenge. Heard from Thomas Pastitshi, Utshimassits, and Philip Michel, Sheshashui.

How Manish and His Son Were Killed. Philip Rich, Utshimassits.

Katshiuas. Flying skeletons are somewhat rare in Innu lore. They are less rare in Cree lore, where they operate under the name *pakak*. Not surprisingly, the narrator of this story, Gabriel Noah (Utshimassits), grew up in

Fort Chimo, Quebec, among the Little Whale Cree.

Beard-Heart. Bearded or hairy *atcens* seem to suggest the presence of Euro-Canadians, especially the early *voyageurs,* who were not altogether genteel in their dealings with Native people.

IV. ANIMALS

Atikwapeo. From a conversation with Apinam Ashini, Sheshashui. Atikwapeo is not unlike an animal master (see my note for "Niassa") in his managing of caribou affairs.

The Mucawaunipi (George River) caribou herd is by far the largest caribou herd in Eastern Canada.

The Hunter and the Geese. One of the most popular of all Innu tales. This version was told by Tshinish Pasteen, Utshimassits.

Metcimiu. Matthew Rich, Sheshashui.

The First Loon. Michikimau, a lake sacred to the Innu, vanished in 1963 owing to the Churchill Falls Hydro Project. *Sic transit gloria mundi!*

The Origin of Robins. This northern variant of the Oedipus myth was narrated by Thomas Pastitshi, Utshimassits.

Storm. Anyone who doubts the veracity of this story has never set foot in interior Labrador. To do so is to be sucked slowly, relentlessly, insidiously dry. Yet a case can be made for the mosquito as the ultimate Labrador conservationist, determined at all costs)—often giving up its very life—to drive away human beings and thus preserve one of the last truly wild environments in North America.

Ushkeu's Anger. Heard from John Michel, Sheshashui. The Innu consider it a species of blasphemy to let fat touch the ground at a *mukoshan.*

How the Birds of Summer Were Brought North. Spliced together from versions told by Tshinish Pasteen, Philip Rich, and John Poker, Utshimassits. Algonquin-speaking peoples who live south of the St. Lawrence River—the Abenaki, for instance, or the Penobscot—identify Ursus Major with the bear. The Innu, however, identify it with the fisher *(Martes pennanti)* and refer to the constellation as *wetceketek,* or Fisher Star.

V. Magic and Taboos

The Shit Man. Told by Uinipapeu Rich, Utshimassits. This tale seems to have disconcerted Harvard anthropologist William Duncan Strong so sufficiently that his 1928 manuscript version of it is as sanitized as a Harvard class syllabus.

The Haunted Lodge. Only the Innu version of this tale—a not uncommon one among Algonquin speakers—has an ending seemingly manufactured by Jorge Luis Borges.

The Origin of Spruce Sap. Uinipapeu Rich, Utshimassits. *Pitsu* means "spruce sap." Many of the Innu use it as a substitute for chewing gum.

The Man Who Used His Son for Bait. Matthew Rich, Sheshashui.

Napao. The Innu believe that certain dreams will hold you prisoner until you die from them. Here Napao has fallen victim to one of these dreams. On another level, he seems to have fallen victim to tuberculosis, a disease endemic among the Innu even today. Thomas Pastitshi, who told me this little anecdote, was suffering from tuberculosis himself.

A Head of Lice. Told by John Poker, Utshimassits.

Why Some People Starved Near Indian House Lake. Indian House Lake used to be one of the most favored rendezvous places for the Innu in interior Labrador.

Sheshin. Anthropologist Frank Speck writes (in *Naskapi):* "As soon as the beast is dispatched, the hunters collect themselves about the carcass and light their pipes for a libation of smoke. And they do not slight the victim, for ... the old order of conduct toward the bear required them to put some tobacco in his mouth or make a pipe of birch bark, and putting a charge of tobacco in it, insert it in the victim's mouth for a friendly smoke with his conquerors."

Where Thunder Comes From. Collected from Gabriel Noah, Utshimassits. Other versions of this tale (Frank Speck's, for example) are more culinary: the fish are not burned up but cooked en masse and thus provide the people with a sort of meteorological feast.

The Little Man. Narrated by Gilbert Rich, Utshimassits. In the shaking tent ceremony *(kwoshapatcigan),* the *mistapeo* sits inside a four-pole, cylindrical tent and calls on his helping spirits to assist him in some shamanic venture. The Innu probably learned about shaking tents from the Cree in Fort Chimo, Quebec, where both formerly traded. There hasn't been a shaking tent in Labrador in at least fifteen years, a testimony, I suspect, to its imported nature rather than the dying out of a tradition.

VI. TCHAKAPESH

The Birth of Tchakapesh. Told by Tshinish Pasteen, Philip Rich, and Uinipapeu Rich, Utshimassits. Although Tchakapesh bears some familial resemblance to northern culture heroes like Glooscap (Micmac), Wasahketchuk (Cree), Nanabozho (Ojibwa), and Snowy Owl (Penobscot), his pedigree may very well be older than any of these worthies—perhaps dating as far back as the last Ice Age. For that's when woolly mammoths and *homo sapiens* coexisted on the North American continent. Whether you believe Tchakapesh (or a proto-

149

Tchakapesh) goes back that far mostly depends on how you interpret the word *katcitouhuskw.* Scholars have translated it variously as "stiff-legged bear," "sharp-toothed beast," and "great beast." On the other hand, the Innu themselves insist that the word means "long nose." What oversized, long-nosed animal other than a mammoth, they ask, could have disposed of Tchakapesh's parents so expertly? What other over-sized, long-nosed animal sports tusks? Since it's their tradition, I'll defer to them and, in so doing, call attention to a line of storytelling that runs the gamut of the Pleistocene.

How Tchakapesh Got Rid of Some Giants. The woodpecker referred to here is the Northern Three-toed Wood-pecker *(Picoides tridactylus),* the only woodpecker that seems reasonably comfortable in the boreal woods of Labrador. Sometimes, when you're walking through these woods, the only sound you hear is the CLACK! CLACK! CLACK! of this bird excavating a dead trunk.
   "Gaskamu atomua!" (You eat dog!") is the worst in-sult, next to *"Atomua ak!"* ("You're a dog's cunt!"), in the Innu language.

Tchakapesh Gets Married. Collected from Uinipapeu Rich and John Poker, Utshimassits. In another version of this tale, the girls, instead of marrying Tchakapesh, try to eat him.

Tchakapesh and the Crow. It's hard to say which bird, crow or raven, Tchakapesh is punishing in this story, for both birds are commonly called crows *(kakatsheu)* by the Innu.

Why Salmon Are Always Swimming Up Falls. From Thomas Pastitshi, Utshimassits.

Why Ice Cracks in the Winter. This children's tale, told by Mary Michel (Sheshashui), has an obvious purpose: to keep kids off the ice in the winter.

The Departure of Tchakapesh: A Conversation. From a conversation with Gilbert Rich, Utshimassits, recorded August 25, 1988. In another version of this story, which I heard from Uinipapeu Rich, Tchakapesh lassoes the moon with a rope made from his sister's pubic hair.

BIBLIOGRAPHY

Cabot, W. B. *Labrador.* Boston: Small, Maynard & Company, 1920.

Desbaraits, Peter. *What They Used To Tell About.* Toronto: Maclellan and Stewart, 1969.

Low, A. P. *Report on Explorations in the Labrador Peninsula.* Ottawa: Geological Survey of Canada, 1896.

Speck, Frank. *Naskapi.* Norman: University of Oklahoma Press, 1935.

Strong, William Duncan. Unpublished manuscript from the MacMillan-Field Expedition, 1927–1928.

Turner, Lucien. *Ethnology of the Ungava District.* Washington: Smithsonian Institution, 1889–1890.

Wallace, Dillon. *The Long Labrador Trail.* New York: The Outing Publishing Company, 1935.

152

Lawrence Millman, pictured above with Innu storyteller John Poker, is the author if seven previous books, including the Eskimo folktale collection *A Kayak Full of Ghosts*. His travel book about the North, *Last Places*, has been called "a classic of the genre" by the *Sunday Times* (London), while his novel *Hero Jesse* was a Finalist for the 1982 PEN/Hemingway Award. He lives in Cambridge, Massachusetts.

EXPLORING THE
QUANTOCK HILLS
WITH CHRIS CHAPMAN

NOEL ALLEN & CAROLINE GIDDENS

A CHANNEL
FOUR BOOK

SUTTON PUBLISHING

First published in 1994 by
Sutton Publishing Limited
Phoenix Mill · Thrupp · Stroud · Gloucestershire · GL5 2BU
in association with
HTV Limited and Channel 4 Television Corporation

Reprinted 1995, 1996, 1997

British Library Cataloguing-in-Publication Data

Allen, N.V.
  Exploring the Quantock Hills with Chris Chapman
  I. Title II. Giddens, Caroline
  914.238504

ISBN 0-7509-0738-X

Cover pictures: *front*: Chris Chapman on the Quantocks; *back*: East
Quantoxhead.

 ALAN SUTTON™ and SUTTON™ are the trade
marks of Sutton Publishing Limited

Typeset in 10/13 Times.
Typesetting and origination by
Sutton Publishing Limited.
Printed in Great Britain by
Ebenezer Baylis, Worcester.

Contents

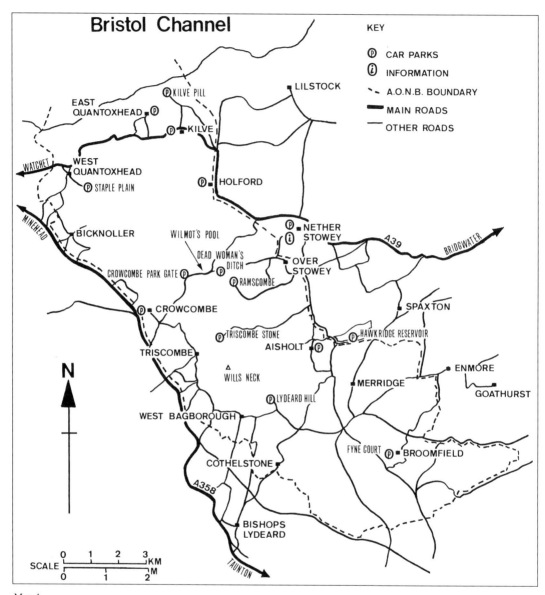

Map 1
The Quantocks. (Drawn by Jonathan White.)

Introduction

The Quantock range of hills lies in the western part of Somerset midway between Bridgwater and Minehead. The hills form a clearly defined feature rising somewhat abruptly out of the Bristol Channel at Quantoxhead and running southwards for 12 miles to the outskirts of the county town of Taunton. Averaging some 4 miles wide the hills cover an area of 50 square miles. Much of this is over 1,000 ft above sea level with Wills Neck the highest point at 1,261 ft. In Domesday Book of 1087 the name is written 'Cantoche' and is probably derived from a Saxon word for a rim or ridge, a brief but fair description of the Quantocks. Because of their prominence they once linked Dunkery Beacon on Exmoor with the Mendip hills in a line of warning beacons running across England. Their national significance today is that in 1957 the Quantocks were the first area in England to be designated an Area of Outstanding Natural Beauty.

In many ways the Quantocks is a varied and delightful land: of open moorland and sheltered wooded valleys, or combes as they are usually called in the West Country; of rolling, grass foothills and hidden villages; a land of sheep and cattle, and of wild red deer, badger and fox. It is ideal country for walking and riding with all its plant and wildlife interest, its old mansions and parkland, and vast and glorious views. West to the neighbouring Brendon Hills and to the heights of Exmoor, east across Sedgemoor to Glastonbury and the Mendips, north over the Bristol Channel to its islands and the coast of Wales, and south into the patterned Vale of Taunton and the Blackdown Hills. Often all these can be seen with no more than a turn of the head.

For some years the Quantocks had a close association with two of our best known poets, William Wordsworth and Samuel Coleridge, and with other literary men like Charles Lamb, William Hazlitt, De Quincey, Robert Southey and Henry Newbolt, and scientists Andrew Crosse and Sir Humphrey Davy, friend of Tom Poole the tanner of Nether Stowey. Today the Quantock landscape is still marked by Bronze Age barrows erected around 2000 BC, by Iron Age hill forts, by beacons whose flame gave warning of the Armada, and by village churches which through long centuries have borne testimony to the Christian faith.

Getting to the Quantocks

From this brief introduction you will see that the Quantock countryside is well worth getting to know, and its glorious scenery, extensive views, and varied wildlife, should not be missed. The M5 is only a few miles from the Quantocks, and the A39 from Bridgwater and the A358 from Taunton, both going to Minehead, almost encircle the foothills. Regular bus services run from Taunton to Minehead and a few from Bridgwater, passing through a number of villages, and the West Somerset Railway stations at Williton, Stogumber, Crowcombe and Bishop's Lydeard are all within an hour's walk of the hills. Two minor roads actually pass over the hills; one from Crowcombe to Nether Stowey, and another from Cothelstone to Broomfield, the only village on the high ground, and on to Enmore.

Somerset County Council employs two wardens to watch over the Quantocks, to prevent damage to the countryside, and to help and advise visitors. The wardens are based in the library at Nether Stowey where they have an office, information and display room. This is well worth a visit. Telephone (0278) 732845.

Parking places

As most visitors today are likely to arrive by car we list below fifteen of the best parking places. These are either good starting points for walks or are near villages and places of special interest. Here a word of warning must be added: don't leave any valuables in your car, lock everything else in the boot, and remember it is an offence under the 1988 Road Traffic Act to drive more than 15 yd off a public road.

Aisholt (GR ST194356). Car park above church with footpath leading down through the conservation churchyard.

Broomfield (GR ST223321). Car park in grounds of Fyne Court, headquarters of Somerset Wildlife Trust. Information, shop and nature trail.

Crowcombe (GR ST140367). Car park behind Church House facing church.

Crowcombe Park Gate (GR ST151378). Parking just off road

Court House and church, East Quantoxhead. (Photograph by Lesley Thomas.)

above Rams Combe. Ideal for visiting Wilmot's Pool and Hurley Beacon, and walking along ridge road to Triscombe Stone.

Dead Woman's Ditch (GR ST162382). This name appears on maps by 1782. Car park and information board by roadside. Fairly level walk to Iron Age Dowsborough hill-fort and to Wilmot's Pool.

East Quantoxhead (GR ST137436). Car park opposite village millpond. Box for church funds. Circular walk to coast, Kilve Pill and return across fields by Kilve church and chantry ruins.

Hawkridge Reservoir (GR ST206360). Parking in lay-by with view of reservoir. Good for winter waterfowl and summer nesting birds.

Holford Green (GR ST154412). Parking on edge of green. Ideal for visiting Holford Glen and walking through village and Alfoxton Park.

Kilve (GR ST148428). Car park behind village hall opposite the Hood Arms.

Kilve Pill (GR ST145444). Parking near sea opposite cricket ground. Best place for walking along cliffs and getting to the beach and rock pools.

Lydeard Hill (GR ST181338). Car park with fine viewpoints. Fairly level walk to Wills Neck at 1,261 ft, the highest point on the Quantocks.

Nether Stowey (GR ST189396). Car park by library at top of Castle Street. Largest Quantock village, with cottage home of Coleridge owned by National Trust and open April to early October.

Rams Combe (GR ST169376). A most attractive Forestry Commission picnic area, car park and toilets, situated by stream in forest clearing. About 2 miles south of Over Stowey, but you may need a map to get there.

Staple Plain (GR ST116411). Minor road leads up from centre of village by Staple Farm and becomes a track. Parking area is beyond large beech tree, overlooking Weacombe Combe. Fine views and walking.

Triscombe Stone (GR ST164359). Two miles south of Nether Stowey take road into Cockercombe at hamlet of Plainsfield. Car park at end of road above Triscombe. Extensive views over valley to Brendon Hills and Exmoor. Easy walk to Wills Neck about half a mile away.

Walking the Quantocks

In addition to the six main walks detailed in this book, many other walks can be planned by using the Ordnance Survey Pathfinder series of maps. Those covering the Quantocks are: Watchet Sheet ST 04/14 dealing with the coastal region, Quantock Hills Sheet ST 03/13 covering all the central area, and Bridgwater Sheet ST 23/33 covering the eastern part. These maps show almost all the rights of way. In addition, many walks are also signposted and colour coded:

Public Footpath. Yellow. Walkers only.

Bridleway. Blue. Walkers and riders on horses and bicycles.

Rupp. Red. For roads used as public paths (Rupp) where the right is on foot, horseback, bicycle, or motor vehicle.

A few circular walks are indicated by a white arrow encircled in green.

An invalid carriage is not classified as a motor vehicle and may be used on a footpath, though in many places this may not be practical. The law permits horses, donkeys and mules to be ridden along bridleways. It is not clear if you can ride a camel or elephant!

As well as these rights of way there is public access on moorland owned by the National Trust, and the Forestry Commission normally permit walkers on their forest tracks. Much of the northern half of the Quantocks is common land where only registered commoners have special rights, but here the landowners usually permit walkers.

At all times have respect for the countryside and courtesy to other users. Take all litter home, keep dogs under control, fasten all gates and prevent damage to crops. Leave all wild flowers for others to enjoy, and do not molest wild or farm animals. Keep the Country Code and you and others will enjoy and benefit from this lovely part of our land.

CHAPTER ONE

Geology and the Coastal Region

ome knowledge of the geology of the Quantocks is the key to understanding how the landscape was shaped and the vegetation cover developed. These in turn have affected the wildlife, farming and industry, even the building materials, and much of our present-day recreational activities. We come to the Quantocks for we love the hills and valleys, the wide views, the changing colours of moor and woodland, the wild red deer and the delightful villages.

The underlying rocks of the Quantocks belong to what geologists term the Devonian period, and are similar to those under much of Devon and Exmoor. The oldest Devonian rocks which are exposed on the Quantocks are a small outcrop known as the Lynton Beds near Crowcombe, followed by the Hangman Grits, the Ilfracombe Beds and last of all the Morte Slates.

The Lynton Beds are a fine-grained brownish-grey siltstone in which marine fossils have been discovered in the past. Hangman Grits are found in the northern half of the Quantocks and consist largely of a quartz sandstone. The name comes from a similar rock strata at Great and Little Hangman, rising above Combe Martin in north Devon. Its structure consists of gritty sediments laid down under water long ago and then slowly compressed into solid rock. This was eventually subjected to immense pressures forcing the rock upwards where, faced by erosion from rain, frost, storm and ice, it slowly developed into the ridge of hills we see today. Hangman Grits make up much of the higher moorland with high points at Wills Neck, 1,261 ft, and Robin Upright's Hill, 1,171 ft. Here the soil is acid with a vegetative covering of heathers, gorse and moorland grasses. The western escarpment is particularly steep with deep, short combes where whortleberry and, in places, rhododendron have intruded.

There was a time when the sea inundated the central part of the Quantocks and when silt and mud was deposited on top of the earlier

1

Hangman Grits forming the Ilfracombe Beds. These rocks are of special interest for they are made up of limestones, slates and tuff, a kind of fragmentary volcanic rock. This occurs around Cockercombe and the grey-green stone can be seen in the gatehouse leading to Quantock School, once the home of Lord Taunton, in Over Stowey parish. The limestone of this central area supports a varied and interesting flora, quite different to that which grows on the acid moorland.

The southern part below Cothelstone is formed mainly of Morte Slates, a mixture of slate, silts and sandstones which are the youngest rocks on the Quantock hills. Slate does not seem to have been exploited commercially here unlike that on the nearby Brendon Hills, where it was quarried from as early as the fourteenth century to the twentieth century. These softer, southern slates have weathered into lower and more rounded hills with a rich soil more suitable for agriculture.

It is at Triscombe, near Crowcombe that the largest quarrying enterprise takes place. It can come as a shock, after the serenity of walking the moorland, to suddenly find oneself above the busy workings. Looking down from above, one can see roadways cut out of the quarry sides with trucks winding their way along amid clouds of dust, and hear the steady grinding of the pulverizing machinery which reduces the blasted blocks of sandstone weighing several tons to gravel, for spreading upon our roads. The terrific depth of the quarry is partly due to restrictions preventing its further development into the hills, leaving downwards the only way to continue. However, the present plans are for it to close in 1998.

Geology of the Coast

Having given a brief description of the geology of the upland area, there remains a most interesting section still to describe. This is the Quantock coastal region which provides a complete contrast. Here erosion still continues, as can be witnessed along the cliffs and seashore. The beach can be reached by footpaths leading from below East Quantoxhead and Kilve where some of the finest Blue Lias cliffs in the country may be viewed, although they are not always easily accessible. At low tide, however, the spectacular foreshore with its stretches of limestone pavement can be reached and the cliff strata of alternating layers of limestones and shales seen. Cracks, or joints, and a certain amount of slippage are visible. The relentless

Fossil ammonites *Arnioceras* and *Planorbis*. (Drawings by Jonathan White.)

Kilve Beach and cliffs.
(Photograph by Chris
Chapman.)

pounding of the sea gradually eats its way into the foot of the
cliffs undercutting them until, with a resounding crash, another
portion becomes separated and plummets to the shore. Viewed
from above, the cliff top shows fissures where the next falls are
likely to occur, and for this reason it is unwise to venture too close
to the edge.

Returning to the beach, it should be said that these rocks are of the
Jurassic period, a later formation than the Devonian upland section.
It will be seen that many contain fossil remains of animals,
particularly ammonites (*Arnioceras* sp.). These were prehistoric
marine molluscs with coiled shells. Most of the specimens to be
found are quite small, perhaps a couple of inches in diameter, but
they could grow up to 2 ft or more across and sections of these
enormous fossils can be found embedded here and there. Snail-like
molluscs carrying shells 4 ft wide were fact and not confined to
science fiction. Would-be collectors should note, however, that

3

hammering of the cliff face to obtain geological specimens is not permitted as, in addition to the conservation angle, this can cause serious erosion and there is danger from falling rocks. Small rock pieces already detached and fallen on the beach can be closely examined.

Life on the Seashore

Twice daily the tide floods and recedes from this Quantock coastline. At low tide, areas of shingle and sand are uncovered around St Audries Bay and Blue Ben, a promontory formed from the Blue Lias rock. The pavement which forms the majority of the beach is worn into curious shapes with many rock pools. After winter rains several waterfalls cascade onto the shore, some emerging dramatically through holes in the cliff face. It is along the stretch of beach below Kilve that the ancient sport of 'glatting' – hunting conger eels with dogs and canes – took place until recent years. Some eels can be quite terrifying creatures weighing more than 50 lb, and their needle-like teeth can inflict nasty wounds. By day they hide in pools and rock crevices, emerging at night, but now they no longer occur in such size or numbers. Pictures of the old sport of glatting can be seen in the Hood Arms at Kilve. There is, however, still good beach fishing for cod and other fish.

The rock pools provide homes for a variety of maritime creatures such as sea anemones, crabs and shellfish. The only noticeable plants which can withstand the daily submergence in salt water are seaweeds, predominantly wracks, sea lettuce and laver.

A number of birds feed on the beach or stand on the rocks waiting for a change of tide. Gulls: herring, black-headed, and greater black-backed are the commonest, sometimes joined by lesser black-backed which breed on Steep Holm, the island to be seen offshore. Black-and-white oystercatchers are regular visitors and can be observed probing their red bills among the rocks in search of shellfish. Mottled-brown curlews with long, curved bills stroll slowly along, sometimes uttering their plaintive cry, while ringed plovers and dunlin dart here and there busily working their way along the tide line. The tiny rock pipit searches among decaying seaweeds for insects and is often joined by the pied wagtail. Shelduck are regular and colourful visitors and carrion crows, too, often feed on the shore, prising limpets from the rocks with their strong bills. Passage migrants which follow the coast include waders like redshank, whimbrel, godwit and sanderling, also wheatear and yellow wagtail along the cliff tops. Sometimes a peregrine falcon will swoop down and capture a small wader, thus creating a flurry of swift excitement.

On the Cliff Top

The flash of the white rump of the migrant wheatear is sure to give it away as it slips over bank or hedgerow. A few pairs stop to nest near the coast and on the moorland. Birds which may be encountered at any time of year include linnets, goldfinches, yellowhammers, skylarks and meadow pipits.

Few plants grow on the face of these cliffs but the cliff top is a good hunting ground for botanists. It is a great pity that a section of the grassland between the mouth of Kilve Pill and Quantock's Head below East Quantoxhead has been reseeded, particularly now farmers are being encouraged and paid to leave land 'set aside' and uncultivated. That said, the majority of the way between Blue Ben and Lilstock is a delight and the arable fields are not without interest. The path between the fields and the sea is shielded from the prevailing wind on the seaward side by a thick hedge of bramble and blackthorn, ideal habitat for butterflies and small nesting birds such as dunnock, whitethroat, wren and robin.

Some of the plants are quite spectacular, such as the greater knapweed (*Centaurea scabiosa*) with its deep magenta flower-heads, the tall teasels (*Dipsacus fullonum*), the feathery wild carrot (*Daucus carota*) and Jack-go-to-bed-at-noon (*Tragopogon pratensis*) which really does close its yellow flower-heads at mid-day. An alternative name is goat's-beard. Other cliff-top plants to be found here include bristly ox-tongue (*Picris echioides*), a yellow, dandelion type of flower-head with oval leaves covered with sharp bristles, each growing from a whitish patch; its close relation, rough hawkbit (*Leontodon hispidus*) is also to be found. Other typical grassland plants here are slender knapweed (*Centaurea nemoralis*), agrimony (*Agrimonia eupatoria*) and rest-harrow (*Ononis repens*). This is so named because its tangled roots and stems caused problems to the farmers when it became entwined with the tines of the harrow in the days of horse-power. Wild madder (*Rubia peregrina*) is a coastal plant in south and west England, a relative of the cultivated madder (*R. tinctorum*) once grown to use in dyeing cloth.

The water which emerges on the beach at Kilve Pill drains from the Quantock heights, and has traversed Hodder's Combe and Holford Glen before reaching its outlet where there is a thick jungle of willow carr together with a small amount of reed (*Phragmites australis*). Between here and Lilstock, in the right seasons, many more wild flowers may be encountered: cowslips (*Primula veris*), which the gypsies used to gather and sell in bunches from door to door, sea wormwood (*Seriphidium maritimum*), sea pearlwort (*Sagina maritima*), the poisonous deadly nightshade (*Atropa belladonna*), common spotted orchids (*Dactylorhiza fuchsii*), bittersweet (*Solanum dulcamara*) and sea beet (*Beta vulgaris* subsp. *maritima*). A small, white-flowered clover which grows in short grass is fenugreek (*Trifolium ornithopodioides*). A small tree, able to withstand the buffetings of the salt-laden sea breezes is tamarisk (*Tamarix gallica*). Note that it has very tiny leaves; this reduces water evaporation and damage by the wind, thus enabling it to survive on the coast.

One most noticeable plant which grows in profusion on the cliff tops and in the hedgerows approaching the sea is alexanders (*Smyrnium olusatrum*). This is one of the family of Umbellifers, and has greenish-yellow flower-heads which emit a rather pungent smell attractive to many flies and small insects. It was originally introduced from the Mediterranean, hence its name from the Egyptian seaport. It was used by some of the monastic orders as a pot-herb, and in 1562 the botanist, Turner, found it on Steep Holm where there had been a small religious house in the Middle Ages. Its shiny leaves often succumb to attack by a rust fungus, which distorts and marks the foliage with unsightly orange spots.

Coastal Farmland

The coastal farmland is mainly arable and the stubble fields sometimes produce some of the now uncommon and decreasing wild flowers associated with cornfields of old, for example, corn poppy (*Papaver rhoeas*), and in 1993 a single specimen of rough poppy (*P. hybridum*) was found, the first since 1896! Corn spurrey (*Spergula arvensis*) and sharp- and round-leaved fluellen (*Kixia elatine* and *K. spuria*) are less conspicuous, but the latter are well worth getting on hands and knees for; the tiny yellow and purple flowers, with a long spur protruding behind the flower-head, are exquisite. The well-known scarlet pimpernel (*Anagallis arvensis*) abounds but there is also a blue variety to be sought. Milk-thistle (*Silybum marianum*) has striking prickly leaves veined in a white milky colour, and the flower-head is armed with a ruff of inch-long spikes.

Cliff-top butterflies include the handsome marbled white whose caterpillars feed on various grasses, jewel-like blues – holly blue in spring and common blue in summer – and in good years the migratory painted lady and clouded yellow which fly over from the Continent.

Rabbits nibble the foliage and have their burrows right on the cliff edge and no doubt the occasional fox will seek them out, but dog owners should guard against their pets making a dash over the cliff edge after buck rabbit. Slow-worms, the legless lizards so often mistaken for snakes and killed by unthinking people, can often be encountered underneath stones in warm sheltered areas, but please replace the stones carefully.

Coastal Villages

Besides being rather remote, the seaboard side of the Quantocks is only 4 miles with space for three coastal villages, though none are directly by the sea. These are East Quantoxhead, Kilve and Lilstock, and it seems appropriate to consider them here.

We will start at East Quantoxhead (GR ST137436) in the west where two narrow country roads a few hundred yards apart lead towards the sea from the A39 and wind down for just over half a mile before joining up in front of the large village millpond. On the left is a small car park and a contribution box for church funds. Beyond the pond and looking out towards the sea is the grey stone Court House, nestling alongside the church of St Mary. All this makes an idyllic setting virtually unchanged through the centuries, except the village blacksmith, bakehouse, general shop, miller – Mrs Elizabeth Wake was both baker and miller in 1897 – and the inn called the New Inn, are now all but memories. At the top of the east linking road is the remains of the village pound and, running parallel, a stream from the hills feeds into the millpond home of ducks and moorhens, overshadowed by a large black poplar. The road is suitably known as Frog Street, and on the left-hand side is the stone village hall, erected in 1913 by Mrs Alice Luttrell complete 'with a library of 500 volumes and provision for baths'.

The Luttrells have owned Court House ever since Andrew Luttrell proved his right to the manor in 1232. Before this their Paynell ancestors by marriage had been in possession since the Norman Conquest. The present solid and fortress-looking Court House dates mainly from the sixteenth and seventeenth centuries and is now the chief residence of the Luttrells. Their other home, Dunster Castle, was handed over to the National Trust in 1976. The gardens of Court House are occasionally opened to the public, but not the house. A

Old thatched mill house, East Quantoxhead. (Photograph by Lesley Thomas.)

footpath leading behind the millpond passes by the old thatched mill, and then goes by the side of Court House gardens and down to the sea.

The parish church of St Mary is a rather plain grey building with a fourteenth-century tower. The chancel was largely rebuilt in 1860 during a general restoration of the church. Points of interest include the fifteenth-century screen, the Elizabethan pulpit with good foliage carving, some unusual bench ends, and on the north side of the chancel the tomb of Sir Hugh Luttrell, who died in 1522, and his son Andrew. Most of the Luttrell monuments are in the church at

The ruined chantry at Kilve.
(Photograph by Chris
Chapman.)

Dunster. Alexander Fownes Luttrell was rector of East Quantoxhead for seventy-one years from 1818 to 1889.

Kilve (GR ST149429) occupies the centre of the Quantock seaboard. The name comes from an Old English word for cliff, a special feature of the coastline here. The centre of the village straddles the busy A39 where the stream from Holford Glen passes under the road on its way to the sea. Here is the village hall (with a car park) built by the rector in 1885, and behind stands the square, stone-walled Kilve Court erected in 1785 and now a Somerset Council Residential Education Centre. On the other side of the road is the white-painted Hood Arms and attached is a combined general shop and post office. The water-mill, for centuries an essential part of village life, is now a house named Kilve Mill. The upper part of Kilve is generally know as Putsham; there is a Putsham Farm here, or Potsdam as Dorothy Wordsworth called it in her *Journal*. Pardlestone Lane comes down from the hills, passes by Alfoxton, the Quantock home of the Wordsworths, crosses the A39 near the

Hood Arms and, accompanied by the stream, continues for another mile as Seaward Lane to the beach.

St Mary's church stands near the end of the lane, with a low, embattled tower looking quite ancient but probably rebuilt in the seventeenth century according to a worn inscription. The font is Norman, and a section of the old rood-screen leans against a tower wall. A wide arch in the north chancel wall almost certainly led into a chantry founded in 1329 by the lord of the manor, Sir Simon de Fourneaux. Just below are the ivy-covered ruins of a medieval manor-house given to accommodate five priests responsible for the chantry services. A watercolour painted in 1847 reveals the house to be a substantial building. Shortly afterwards it was seriously damaged by fire aided, it was rumoured, by kegs of brandy stored away by smugglers. This isolated stretch of coast from Watchet to Bridgwater was for long a favourite landing-place for contraband goods. A square, red-brick building with an iron chimney closer to the beach is a retort, erected in 1914 when efforts were made to extract oil from the rocks. Oil does lie in the rocks here, but the cost of extraction has so far made all attempts uneconomical.

Oil retort, Kilve. (Drawing by Jonathan White.)

Kilve beach with its rocky foreshore, freshwater stream, cliffs and walks, is a popular place on a summer afternoon. There is a convenient parking area nearby plus the village cricket ground. This was a favourite spot for Coleridge and the Wordsworths, and William wrote of 'Kilve's delightful shore'. The splendour of it is that it remains virtually unchanged since the days they walked down the lane from Holford.

Lilstock (GR ST167448), formerly Little Stoke, lies in the north-eastern corner of the Quantocks, on a headland on the Bristol Channel. It is a small hamlet consisting of two or three farms and the tiny church of St Andrew. The former church was pulled down when the parish was ecclesiastically annexed to nearby Kilton in 1881, leaving only the medieval chancel. This was made into a miniature church in the nineteenth century by the addition of a porch and bell-cote. For some time it was used as a mortuary chapel but it then fell into disuse, and on the Pathfinder series of Ordnance Survey maps it states 'remains of' beside the church. However, following his retirement in 1994, the former Rector of Kilve, the Revd Rex Hancock, instigated its renovation and undertook much of the work with loving care. Today it is a bright little church, hopefully soon to have an inaugural service held there. The churchyard is known for its springtime flowers, especially cowslips.

During the Second World War there was a firing range on the

(The restored church of
St Andrew, Lilstock.
Photograph by Chris
Chapman.)

cliffs at Lilstock, where specialist training was given using
Lysanders, Martinets and Masters aircraft.

Hinkley Point (GR ST210460)

Beyond Lilstock, situated on the flat expanse of marshland
overlooking Bridgwater Bay, towers Hinkley Point Nuclear Power
Station. It so dominates this eastern edge of the Quantocks that it
cannot be ignored. The site was chosen for it had the necessary
foundations, a sparse population and the Bristol Channel, which was
able to provide water in abundance for cooling (up to 270 million
litres an hour). Work began on the two reactors of Hinkley 'A'
station in December 1957 and it first supplied electricity to the
National Grid in February 1965. The 'B' station, which is gas
cooled, opened in 1976. Hinkley made history in being the first such
station in the world to produce half a million kilowatts of electricity
for civil use.

The coming of the power station provided jobs for its 1,400 strong workforce who live in the surrounding villages and towns; there were road improvements, and the harbour at Combwich was rebuilt to bring in the required heavy machinery.

Perhaps surprisingly, the station is visited by around 13,000 visitors a year and station staff are on hand to answer queries or provide a free tour of the reactors, control room, turbines and generators. This takes about one and a half hours. There is also a visitor centre and a nature trail.

The nature trail takes about an hour to cover and has a variety of habitats. Nuclear Electric plc is keen to point out that 125 species of lichen have been identified here and that these require a clean air environment in order to flourish. Over 200 species of flowers, trees and ferns also occur, notably bee orchids (*Ophrys apifera*) and pale flax (*Linum bienne*). The company has recorded 11 mammal species, 25 butterfly species and 40 bird species, of which the nightingale may be heard singing on a May evening, its notes echoing plaintively against the hum of the power station.

Beacon Hill to Hinkley Point

This linear walk starts on the high moor near Beacon Hill and drops quickly via Smith's Combe and country lanes to East Quantoxhead. From here field paths lead to the sea's edge and then there is a cliff-top walk to Hinkley Point with short diversions to Kilve Chantry and Lilstock. This is a particularly fascinating walk for anyone interested in either wild flowers or geology but all will enjoy the superb views. Distance: about 8 miles. Maps: ST 04/14 and 24/34.

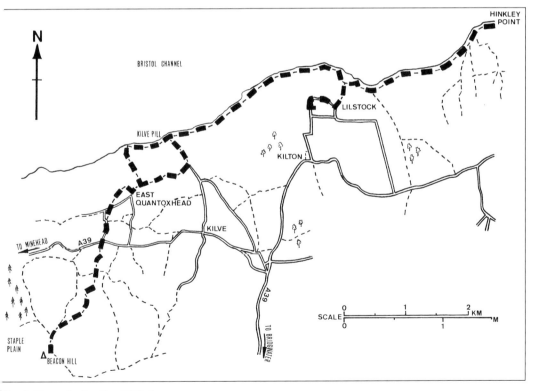

Map 2. (Drawn by Jonathan White.)

Drive to West Quantoxhead and from the centre of the village take the narrow road by Staple Farm to car park on Staple Plain (GR ST116411). Walk forward and take the moorland track that climbs up to the trig. point on Beacon Hill (1,023 ft).

From Beacon Hill there are lovely views in all directions – towards Exmoor to the west, towards Wales to the north and to the Mendips in the east. Whichever way you look, the eye is drawn back to the bulky structures of the Hinkley Point Nuclear Power Station, the finishing point for this walk.

Take the path that heads north towards the coast via Smith's Combe.

At the bottom of the combe the footpath crosses a meadow with a stream flanked by alders, mature oaks, and field-barn buildings that express to perfection one vision of the English countryside.

Cross the A39 at the bottom of the lane – taking great care as there is a blind corner to the right – and follow the narrow country road opposite which winds down to East Quantoxhead. Just before reaching Court Farm pick up the path, again passing over the fields, to the church attached to Court House.

St Mary's church has been described earlier (see p. 8), but there are some smaller details worth looking for. In one side of the porch wall is an aperture rather like an archer's opening in a castle wall. This is known as 'the coffin squint' and is supposed to have been used to observe the imminent arrival of a coffin – presumably in order to cue the service inside. Beside the small priest's door into the chancel there can still be seen the faint marks of a 'scratch dial' – a primitive sundial now lacking its shadow-casting pin at the top – which once would have served the incumbent intent on starting mass on time. At the other end of the building, the stones at the base of the tower show every sign of having been trawled from the seashore below the house where the fault lines cut the Blue Lias rock into handy rows of building blocks.

Turn left outside the church past a fine group of farm buildings that include open-fronted barns still used to house cattle. Continue through the car park to the picturesque duck-pond, home of mallard and moorhen. Skirting the pond follow the path past the former thatched mill house to the bottom of the beautifully kept Court House gardens.

Court House is the home of Sir Walter Luttrell whose family has owned it since 1232, but the present building dates from about 350 years later. The gardens are opened annually to the public, usually in May when a notice is posted on the main gates by the pond.

If you wish to make the diversion to Kilve church and the ruined chantry, follow the alternative path which goes beside the wood and across a field. The chantry has been described (see p. 9) and there are tearooms nearby. If not making the diversion, take the main path which crosses the fields to the cliff edge; where the path turns to the right, drop down to the left just past the ruins of a limekiln and descend the galvanized stairs to the beach.

At this point on the foreshore the amateur geologist is treated to a lesson in earth history. Successive strata of limestone and shale – gold and blue and grey – chase each other up the cliff face, occasional frenzies of activity frozen into stone snapshots of ancient geology. Underfoot, the pale grey limestone pavement appears to have been laid by hand, with its rectangular shapes and sea-washed surface.

Proceed to Kilve Pill ('pill' is a local name for a tidal creek or pool) by either continuing along the beach or reclimbing the stairs and walking along the cliff top, then turn inland for a short distance to the car park which is provided with toilets.

The stream that flows down to the beach here rises on the hills above Holford.

The Texas that never was. By the car park is what must be the ugliest listed building in Britain – a brick-built blockhouse with a rusting iron chimney. It is all that is left of larger installations used to heat the local shale to release its rich oil content. If the experiments in 1914 had proved commercially successful, what would the effect have been on this unspoilt coastline? We need only look along the shore towards Hinkley to receive one kind of answer to this question.

Leave Kilve Pill and continue east along the cliff path.

This next section of the path is marked on Ordnance Survey maps as The Gallops. Map names are curious: whole linguistic, cultural and political histories can be read from some place-names, others have origins lost in the mists of time. But the process can be seen in action at this place – the late father of the present farmer ran a successful National Hunt stables and galloped his horses here until the early 1980s. Now the stables are no more and the ground is ploughed so that galloping is not really feasible, but the name remains to tease future generations of walkers with its meaning.

Out to sea can be seen objects; from afar one of them looks like a small fishing boat, but they are, in fact, the tethered targets of a Royal Naval Aircraft Range. Strike aircraft practise low-level bombing and helicopter gunships engage in live-firing – you see the water spurt as the bullets strike and hear the sound long after the action has finished. A control tower on the cliff top displays a red flag when the range is operational.

Between here and Lilstock Beach is a section which will delight any botanist or lover of wild flowers. The frothy heads of wild carrot mingle with greater knapweed and yellow-wort and there are various orchids and salad burnet, smelling of cucumber. As you near Lilstock the windblown tamarisk trees give a desolate look to the crumbling wartime pillboxes. There is an assortment of grasses which flower in June and July constantly moving in the sea breezes.

Lilstock Beach, like Kilve, is an unspoilt stretch of a stony shoreline where people come to fish, walk and look for fossils. But the similarity is deceptive. Kilve has never been developed; Lilstock was once a thriving little port with harbour walls which are still evident and quayside houses including a hotel, and a great sluice-gate that was opened periodically to flush out the mooring channel, which now has its entrance blocked with pebbles.

Remainders of this past are still visible on the ground but most are thickly overgrown with shrubs and trees. There are old photographs showing the extent of the harbour and its associated buildings. Here too, in the nineteenth century, was the summer house of the Acland family from nearby Fairfield House. Fanny, the wife of Sir Peregrine Acland and four of their small children died of tuberculosis, but their daughter Harriet – born in 1832 – survived the illness by spending all her days at the summer house exposed to the cleansing breezes from the Atlantic. As a thank-offering for her life, Sir Peregrine built the school in Stogursey in 1860. The ornate building carries an inscription over the doorway proclaiming this.

> **If you wish to view Lilstock village and church a short detour should be made from here along the main track leading inland and then return to take the adjoining track which runs beside a line of trees and emerges again on the cliff edge where the path continues towards Hinkley Point.**

This section of the path has been made a special area by the Countryside Commission for the growth of the coastal flowers. Until recently the arable crops grew to the very edge of the path, but a width of 20 yd adjacent to the path has been sown with a special grass mix designed to allow the natural coastal flowers to seed into it in future.

> **In a short distance the path reaches Hinkley Point.**

Hinkley 'A' and Hinkley 'B' raise important questions for walkers, conservationists and others who are interested in the well-being of the rural environment. Quite apart from the issue of nuclear power itself, there are questions of siting, local economics and aesthetics to be considered. Hinkley 'A' was designed by Frederick Gibberd, distinguished architect of Stevenage new town, the Catholic Cathedral Church of Christ the King in Liverpool, and the mosque in Regent's Park. The panels of the buildings were originally clear so that the workings inside could be seen from outside. But these have been replaced by blue cladding that sits uncomfortably in the grey and brown visual environment of the Bristol Channel. Hinkley 'B' – housing a different kind of reactor technology – was also designed by Gibberd but has the appearance of an enormous corrugated garden shed.

Cowslips. (Drawing by Jonathan White.)

17

At a distance, the blocks of the Gibberd design achieve a certain grandeur that adds something to the bleakness of the coastline, but close to, the walker's experience of the stations cannot be anything other than that of an industrial intrusion on an overwhelming scale.

Offshore, the Holm islands may be seen, Steep Holm being the nearest and Flat Holm with its white lighthouse further off. The promontory running out towards Steep Holm is Brean Down, near Weston-super-Mare.

Note: The walk described above follows Chris Chapman's footsteps in the television programme. If you prefer a circular walk, returning to the starting point, it is suggested that you follow the directions as far as Kilve Chantry and then continue up Sea Lane until the A39 road is reached. Cross the road and continue up Pardlestone Lane and on up Pardlestone Hill until the path is crossed by the Great Road track. Turn right along the track which leads back to the car park on Staple Plain.

If a level, cliff-top walk is desired it is best to park at East Quantoxhead. Follow the directions as far as Lilstock church, then continue on the lane to Kilton and, after passing through the hamlet, take the footpath running through fields to your right. This leads to Sea Lane; turn right again to Kilve church and pick up the footpath opposite the church. This goes back to East Quantoxhead.

CHAPTER TWO

Through the Centuries

Earliest Times

T he Bronze Age period of around 2000 BC saw new groups of people moving into southern England and eventually some settled on the high ground of the Quantocks. Centuries before this the hills must have been hunted by Neolithic man for small numbers of flint arrowheads and simple tools have been found. The Bronze Age people left no written evidence behind, and we have no idea what language they spoke. What they did leave behind were burial mounds or round barrows, often shown as tumuli on maps, and at least sixty have been located on the Quantocks. In addition, small hoards of bronze weapons, ornaments and cooking pots have been discovered at Cothelstone, Stogursey and Spaxton. Many of the barrows have been opened in the past by treasure seekers, who were nearly always doomed to disappointment for the finds usually consisted of a single skeleton and a pottery beaker. From this the ancient folk are often called Beaker People, and these barrows are probably the graves of tribal leaders buried on high ground to keep a guardian watch over their people. Most of the surviving barrows are on open moorland and lie close to the ancient ridgeway running along the crest of the hills. There are several on Thorncombe Hill above Bicknoller, with others on either side of Wilmot's Pool, on Wills Neck and Cothelstone Hill. One of the largest is on Hurley Beacon and measures 90 ft round at the base and 7 ft high.

The Bronze Age period slowly melted into the Iron Age when iron was used for the first time in making weapons and tools, and this covered some 700 years immediately before the Christian era. It was a time which marked the domestication of cattle and pigs in Britain, the growing of cereals, and the building of stone round houses thatched with straw, heather and gorse. It was also a time when tribal raiding was a regular pursuit and when Iron Age people erected huge defensive earthworks into which they retreated when danger threatened.

Two quite impressive Iron Age hill-forts on the Quantocks are Dowsborough (GR ST160392) above Nether Stowey, and Ruborough (GR ST227335), north of Broomfield. Dowsborough lies just off the Holford to Crowcombe road, 1,000 ft up on the edge of Robin Upright's Hill. This defensive earthwork covers 7 acres, much now under scrub oak, and is enclosed by a ditch and rampart 15 ft high. It is a stiff walk up to it from Holford, but from the road the approach is almost level. Half a mile away and right by the road and car park is Dead Woman's Ditch, an Iron Age linear rampart 6 ft high. It was perhaps a part of the outer defences of Dowsborough. Who the dead woman was is not known, but the name appears on the Day and Master's map of Somerset of 1782, seven years before John Walford murdered his wife below Dowsborough in 1789. Ruborough is not so easily found. It stands 700 ft up on a spur of a hill surrounded by the conifer plantation of Heathcombe Wood. It can be reached by a walk of 2 miles from the car park at Fyne Court, Broomfield. The path crosses several fields, then continues along the road, and finally takes a track through the wood. It is worth finding for it is a fine example of a hill-fort, triangular in shape with a single rampart and ditch, the banks 20 ft high and still difficult to climb. Ruborough must have been a formidable obstacle 2,500 years ago when it was topped with a spiked wood palisade.

Other Iron Age works include Trendle Ring (GR ST118394) on a slope of Bicknoller Hill. This is a circular earthwork 100 yd in diameter, but was more likely a herding place for stock rather than a fort. The name seems to have been derived from trundle, a West Country word for a large oval tub used for scalding pigs. An enclosure of 2 acres on the south side of lower Cockercombe may also be an Iron Age hill slope enclosure (GR ST184363).

Romans

The Romans invaded Britain in AD 43 and took fifty years to subdue the native tribes. The north of England was shut off by Hadrian's Wall, and the country west of a line from Exeter to Bristol was never occupied except for brief incursions. In Somerset they settled in two towns: Ilchester, which was a frontier garrison, and Bath, important for its mineral springs and hot baths. They also had a branch road into the Mendips to open up the lead mines. Between AD 50 and AD 65 the Romans maintained two small garrisons in North Devon for keeping watch over the mouth of the Bristol Channel and across to Wales. The earliest was at Old Barrow, above Glenthorne and right on the present Somerset/Devon border, followed by another on the cliffs at Martinhoe. Both have been excavated and the earth ramparts can be visited. It was the fashion in the last century to subscribe some Iron Age forts to the Romans, but there is no conclusive evidence they ever settled on the Quantock Hills. No doubt the swampy heart of Somerset and the Quantock and Exmoor hills restricted them to the more accessible and fertile parts of the country.

Saxons and King Arthur

The departure of the Romans from Britain in AD 410 eventually opened the way for the Saxon invaders who reached Somerset early in the seventh century. This was the age of King Arthur, who rallied the local Celtic tribes in a stern but slowly faltering resistance, and around whose exploits a wealth of legend gathered. Probably Wills Neck, 'the ridge of the Wealas', marks the spot of their final stand. The great ridge road running along the spine of the Quantocks, known as Alfred's Road, a favourite track with riders and walkers, belongs to this period of history. Most of the Saxon kings held land and lodges in Somerset and hunted over the Quantocks. There was a Saxon mint at Watchet, and Bicknoller and Halsway were royal manors. These and other manors developed into the village communities we know today. It was during the sixth century that the Christian faith first arrived in the West Country through the efforts of Celtic missionary saints from Ireland, Wales and Brittany. Early church dedications recall some of their names: Decuman at Watchet, Dubricius at Porlock, Beuno at Culbone, Petrock or Little Peter at Timberscombe. In the reign of Ethelwulf, King of Essex 839–858, the biblical custom of freely giving a tithe or tenth of the crops and stock towards the support of the local church was made compulsory and became part of the common law of the land. A charter of 682 shows that Kentwine, King of the West Saxons, gave land to the Abbot of Glastonbury, 'near the famous wood known as Cantucudu'. This is the earliest known reference to the name Quantock.

The Normans

The invasion of England in AD 1066 by William the Conqueror was not all over with the Battle of Hastings and fighting continued for several more years. To protect their forces as they moved inland the Normans erected a series of temporary defensive works each known as a motte and bailey. These consisted of an oval outer earth rampart, the motte, with an inner raised fort, the bailey. There are the remains of a splendid one at the top of Castle Street in Nether Stowey. As happened over much of England, William the Conqueror divided the Quantock land into fourteen large estates which he allocated to some of his closest followers, keeping Bicknoller and nearby Cannington for himself. Ralph Paynell was given land around Bagborough and at East Quantoxhead where he settled down on the site of the present Court House. In 1232 the manor passed to a descendant, Andrew Luttrell, and more than 750 years later the family still lives there. Most of the other ancient families have gone from their Quantock homes: the Malets from Enmore, Audleys from Stowey Court, Stawells from Cothelstone, and Dodingtons from their hall. Kilve Court is now a youth residential centre, and Crowcombe Court is a retirement home.

John Leland, librarian and antiquarian to Henry VIII, undertook a grand tour of England between 1534 and 1543 with the object of writing a *History and Antiquities of this Nation*. In riding from Bridgwater to Dunster he came to Nether Stowey and on to Quantoxhead and Williton. This is what he wrote:

> From Cannington to Stowey 3 good miles. Stowey a poore village standith in a bottom among hills. Here is a goodly manor place of the Lord Audeley's standith exceeding pleasantly for goodly pastures, and having by it a parke of red deer and another of fallow, and a fair brook serving all the offices of the manor place. The Lord Audeley that received in Henry VII time, began great foundations of stone work to the enlarging of this house, the which yet be seen half imperfect. The river of Stowey riseth in the hills thereby by West, and runneth along through Stowey village goweth after to the sea. The sea is about 4 miles from Stowey. From Stowey to Saint Audries is 5 miles. I left this village a little on the right. It standeth about a mile from the sea. In this parish I saw a fair park and manor place of the Luttrells called Quantock-head, because it standeth at the head of Quantock hills toward the sea. These hills runneth in crests from Quantockhead towards Taunton as from North to south-east. I passed over 2 notable brooks betwixt Stowey and St. Audries that ran from the mountains to the sea.

Troublesome Days

The autocratic rule of Charles I was as much resented in Somerset as elsewhere in England. By the summer of 1642 the towns of Bridgwater, Taunton and Minehead, together with Dunster, decided for Parliament, and at the same time some of the chief landowners, like Sir John Stawell of Cothelstone, Sir Francis Dodington of Dodington Hall and Francis Wyndham of Orchard Wyndham, were for the king. By the end of the year the Royalists were driven out of Somerset, some escaping over to Wales in two small ships from Minehead, and the rest straggled across the hills of West Somerset into Devon and Cornwall. In June 1643 the kings's forces returned, commanded by the Earl of Hertford and reinforced by cavalry and by 4,000 Cornish infantry. This new army met with little resistance; Taunton surrendered on 5 June with hardly a shot fired, and Thomas Luttrell handed over Dunster Castle to his Royalist neighbour Col. Wyndham. With the fall of Bristol at the end of July, Somerset was again in the king's hands and remained so for the next year. Most of the Quantock villages suffered the inevitable levies for money, supplies and forced conscripts, largely carried out by Goring's Royalist men. It was widely reported that Sir Francis Dodington committed atrocities including the murder of a minister on the Taunton road: 'Who art thou for, priest', he demanded, 'For God and His gospel' came the reply, and for this Dodington shot him dead.

These were lawless days and groups of Somerset men, chiefly of the yeoman class and calling themselves Clubmen, formed up into bands to protect their homes and stock from the excesses of the warring parties. They set a watch in every village and at a meeting in 1645 at Triscombe, near Crowcombe, put forward a plan for setting up a balanced government of king and parliament and a church founded on the bible and prayer-book. By now, however, it was too late for compromise as Cromwell's New Model Army advanced into Somerset and decisively defeated the king's forces at Langport on 10 July 1645 within sight of the Quantock hills. Dunster Castle was the last Royalist stronghold in the county and held out till April 1646 when Col. Wyndham surrendered to Robert Blake of Bridgwater after a siege of 160 days.

Most of the landowners who sided with the king were able to recover their estates after payment of heavy indemnities to Parliament. An exception was Sir John Stawell of Cothelstone who was imprisoned for four years, had his manor-house partly pulled down, and his woods and estate sold for £64,000. He survived just

Dodington Hall. (Photograph
by Lesley Thomas.)

long enough to see the Restoration of Charles II in 1660 but, dying
shortly after, was buried in Cothelstone church. Sir Francis
Dodington thought it best to flee to France, where for a time he sold
knives for a living. Eventually he married a wealthy French widow
and returned to his Somerset estates at the Restoration.

The trauma of the Civil War was hardly over when James, Duke
of Monmouth landed at Lyme Regis in Dorset on 11 June 1685, in a
bid to seize the English throne. James II had just succeeded his
brother Charles II, but he was an ardent Roman Catholic, and the
Duke of Monmouth was hailed as the 'Protestant Duke'. Among the
eighty-five followers who arrived with the duke was Thomas Dare, a
goldsmith and alderman of Taunton, and now paymaster to the
expedition. The plan was to march to Taunton gathering recruits on
the way, and to continue across the south Quantock foothills to
Bridgwater and Bristol, expecting by then to have an army strong
enough to advance on London. The duke arrived in Taunton on

18 June with 2,000 men plus 300 horsemen and 4 small cannons. Muskets were handed out and some training given, and two days later the Duke of Monmouth was proclaimed King of England in the market-place. Additional craftsmen and clothiers from the town, and yeomen from the villages around, joined the ranks, most of them believing they were crusading for the Protestant faith and for civil liberty.

It was with a force of nearly 6,000 that the Duke of Monmouth marched out of Taunton on 21 June and, passing through Bridgwater, approached within 5 miles of Bristol. Here an army of 4,000 militia under the Duke of Beaufort barred the way, and Monmouth lacking courage to attack turned away, first towards Bath then back to Bridgwater. By now the king's forces were closing in: 700 cavalry of the Life Guards and Blues, 2,000 regular infantry and 1,500 men of the Wiltshire militia. Through a telescope from the tower of St Mary's church, Bridgwater, Monmouth could see the position of the forces against him, and decided on a surprise night attack. He advanced on the night of 5 July and came within a mile before the alarm was raised. The rebel horsemen were immediately ordered to attack, but meeting with steady musket fire the horses panicked and disappeared from the battlefield. Now Monmouth's footmen rushed to the fight, but were stopped by the wide Bussex Rhine on Sedgemoor and failed to get at close quarters with the royal infantry. Monmouth, believing the battle was lost, fled from the field with a few of his officers. The main body of footmen continued the struggle until dawn when, leaderless and without ammunition, and blasted by artillery, the defiant remnant were overwhelmed by a last cavalry charge.

The losses to the king's army were put at 27 killed and 200 wounded. The rebels losses were about 300 killed in the fighting, and 400 slaughtered in an immediate revenge killing of wounded and escaping men. This included 22 men hanged on trees on the battlefield. In the infamous Bloody Assize under Judge Jeffreys, 330 were executed, 850 transported and 408 imprisoned. Most of those condemned were hanged in their towns and villages, among them 19 at Taunton, 9 at Bridgwater, 3 at Nether Stowey, 3 at Stogumber, 2 at Stogursey and 2 at Cothelstone. Around 2,000 men escaped from the battlefield, some seeking safety near home to be hidden and fed by relatives, many reached the coast and fled to the Continent, and others hid in the Mendip caves and in the more remote parts of the Quantocks and Exmoor. The tragic battle of Sedgemoor, the last to be fought on English soil, and the cruelty that followed still lingers in the memories of many West Country folk. In many ways the awful struggle seems to have been unnecessary, for three years later William of Orange, leader of the Protestant cause in Europe, landed at Brixham, Devon, and James II fled the country.

Mining and Local Riots

Throughout the 1700s various attempts were made to find and extract minerals from the Quantocks, and in 1714 a lease was granted by Mrs Dorothy Luttrell to a group of local adventurers to prospect for copper on Perry Hill, East Quantoxhead. Very little seems to have happened there but more serious work was carried out over forty years in the parish of Dodington, though the results were largely unprofitable and the mines closed in 1802. A final effort, supported by Tom Poole of Nether Stowey, was made between 1817 and 1821, but after an expenditure of £20,000 with only £2,500 received from the sale of ore, this attempt was also closed down. The evidence left today of the mining is two derelict stone engine houses, one in a clump of beech trees, another not far away in a field by the road running down to Dodington, and the mines office, a private residence called The Counting House.

Roland Hill, an itinerant preacher before he was ordained by the bishop of Bath and Wells in 1773, made a preaching tour of Somerset in the summer of 1771. He records in his diary for 10 May:

> At Stowey, to the most outrageous congregation I ever saw. There was such a noise with beating of pans, shovels, etc., blowing of horns and ringing of bells, that I could scarce hear myself speak. Though we were pelted with much dirt, eggs, etc., I was enabled to preach out my sermon. 11th May at Putsham, Kilve, to a serious and attentive congregation out of doors, on Hebrews 2, 17 and 18 on the compassionate unchangeable priesthood of Christ. Though the congregation stood serious, some scoffed at a distance, others threw stones. One man slightly cut, and another almost stunned by a blow which cut him violently over the eye.

The next day was Sunday and after a service in the morning at Kilve he 'rode on to Watchet and preached upon the prodigal son, "I will arise" etc. Luke 15, out of doors with some freedom and power, to some hundreds who behaved with the deepest attention'.

The disturbances experienced by Roland Hill were slight compared with what was to follow, for the years around 1800 were times of serious distress in the Quantock parishes. The high price of bread combined with low agricultural wages led to serious unrest among the poor. A loaf could cost as much as 1s 9d and the farm labourer's weekly wage was not more than 8s. At the end of March 1801 one hundred hungry men set off on a hunger march from the village of Stogursey. In the market-place at Nether Stowey they read out a list of grievances, collected another 100 marchers and set off to find the magistrates, who proved difficult to track down. They arrived in Bridgwater nearly 1,000 strong, unarmed and orderly. Here they issued a demand for all farmers to bring corn to the markets 'at such a price as the baker can sell the quartern loaf at tenpence each'. Then they quietly dispersed to their villages with their mission successful, as Tom Poole wrote to Coleridge at the time:

> We have been in a state of agitation and alarm by riots concerning the price of provision. It began in Devonshire and has gradually travelled the Land's End and upwards to this neighbourhood, so that last week it may have been said that from the Land's End to Bridgwater the whole people had risen en masse. It is not now much otherwise though there is a momentary calm. Here for the present, people have succeeded in lowering the price of provision as follows: the quartern loaf from 21d. to 10d.; butter cheese and bacon from 1s. and 14d. to 8d.; shambles meat from 9d. to 6d. per lb. The men of Stogursey and the neighbouring parishes joined the people here and patrolled the country. they committed no violence, indeed they met with no opposition.

Enclosure of Common Land

For very many years there had been a steady increase in the population of the country and from 1750 it was clear that farming methods were failing to keep up with the need to feed the people. Some improvement was made by introducing root crops, by bringing water-logged ground into production by drainage, and sowing more productive strains of cereals. The root of the problem lay in large areas of land held in common in almost every parish. One third of this lay fallow every year, and the rest was cultivated in long, unfenced strips which often changed hands by lot annually. The government saw the answer to the problems of producing more food in Enclosure Acts, which usually meant that much of the land held in common fell to the big landowners who had the means to enclose it, and farm it more effectively.

Sheep grazing on the hills.
(Photograph by Chris
Chapman.)

Fortunately, much of the high land on the Quantock hills escaped enclosure, and the only major enclosures were 600 acres in Crowcombe parish in 1776, and 1,200 acres in West Bagborough in 1807. Today, nearly half of the hills remain as common land, which means that though the land has a legal owner, others also have a legal right to take some part of the natural produce of the ground. This right consists chiefly of: pasture for grazing a stated number of animals, estovers (taking of firewood and bracken), turbary (the digging of turf or peat for fuel), pannage (feeding of pigs on fallen acorns and beechmast), the right to fish, common of soil, and the taking of stone, sand and gravel. These rights of common may belong to an individual but are chiefly attached to a named farm or house. Nearly one hundred properties in the Quantock parishes have the right of common, which varies from the right to pasture up to 300 sheep, to the right to pasture only 1 horse or 4 sheep. A few houses have the right of estovers and turbary. Taken together there exists the right of pasture for nearly 5,000 sheep, 135 ponies, 80 cattle and 58 goats, but for a variety of reasons less than half of these rights are taken up today. The parishes of Nether Stowey and Over Stowey have registered the right of estovers for their householders. The public have no legal right on common land, except on public rights of way, but it has long been the custom to allow public access on open moorland.

For centuries the villages were largely self-supporting with craftsmen and tradesmen serving the everyday needs of the people. Crowcombe in 1890 had a saddler, carpenter, blacksmith, bootmaker, thatcher, mason, two shopkeepers, butcher, baker, draper, millers, and a post office. The farms needed skilled men – shepherds, horsemen and herdsmen – to care for and work the animals, for even sheep were pressed into service as Sir Thomas Acland reported in 1851, 'Sheep are used as labourers on the farms to eat the grass down close in the fall of the year; and are sometimes marched in close phalanx up and down a ploughed field to tread in the wheat.'

Water flowing off the hills was a cheap source of power and was harnessed for many uses: grinding corn, driving the rollers in the fulling mills where local cloth was cleansed and thickened, cutting hay and roots on farms, and crushing bark used in the tanneries at Nether Stowey and at Holford where the huge wheel remains jutting out above the tannery roof. At Marsh Mills in Over Stowey parish an old mill was rebuilt in 1815 as a silk mill which was in use for twenty years. In Holford Glen there is still the remains of a silk mill probably known to Dorothy Wordsworth for she writes on 27 January 1798, 'The manufacturer's dog makes a strange, uncouth howl. It howls at the murmur of the village stream.'

More Modern Times

A dozen small cottages on Castle Hill, Nether Stowey, were occupied by broomsquires who made and sold brooms in the villages and markets around. The heather, birch and wood for the handles were all available free from the common land, though some of the landowners complained. The Revd Holland met up with some of them on 22 January 1812 as he noted in his diary, 'I rode out this day. Saw some of the Broomers making a new enclosure on the side of the Crowcombe road. They were going to plant potatoes. Know you said I, that I must have Tithe. They intend it, answered they.

They told me that the Palmers were sent to jail for stealing wood.' Only a week before he had met with another problem: 'We had a good deal of bustle about a marriage. Old Savage Ware, past seventy, married to Jane Long, about sixty. Old Ware had lost his teeth and I had hard work to make him pronounce his words right. They were married out of the Poor House but kept their Revelling at Molly Weymouth's of the next door. Ware, though old, is a very laborious hearty workman. His children did not behave well to him and so he married.'

In contrast to the many parish poor living on 8s a week plus a few shillings of parish relief, in the 1850s Henry Labouchere bought up half of Over Stowey and erected a mansion on a wooded hillside, calling it Quantock Lodge. Here he lived in some style with twenty indoor servants and as many more labouring on the estate. In 1835 he stood as a Liberal against the future prime minister Benjamin Disraeli and defeated him. Created Baron Taunton in 1859, he died in 1869 and the title went with him, but the estate continued with his daughter. During the First World War many of the oaks on the estate in some of the loveliest combes of the Quantocks were felled. In 1922 much of the land and Quantock Lodge were bought by Somerset County Council and leased to the Forestry Commission who shrouded much of it with conifers. The house became a sanatorium until 1962 and is now a private school.

The start of the twentieth century saw a gradual improvement in the lives of most Quantock folk but the villages slowly lost most of their craftsmen and tradesmen, and some lost half their population. By 1930 instead of walking to Taunton and Bridgwater many ordinary folk took to cycling, and by 1970 most families possessed a car. For a time many rural cottages became derelict, but over recent years most have been restored and new houses and bungalows built on empty plots. The new stands alongside the old, local folk have newcomers as neighbours, and both are jostled by summer visitors.

To walk up Hurley Beacon and recall the ancient Britons, or to look across to Court House at East Quantoxhead and remember the Norman Paynells and Luttrells, or to pass down Castle Street in Nether Stowey as good Tom Poole and Wordsworth and Coleridge did, to see the Church House at Crowcombe once filled with the village poor, and to pause before the war memorials that stand in every village. To do these and a hundred other things, is to take a long walk through the centuries in Quantock country.

Blackmore Farm to Fyne Court

This linear walk links up a number of the ancient houses of the Quantock area, beginning on the lower ground at Blackmore Farm and climbing to Broomfield, the highest village on the Quantocks. More information about the places visited can be found in chapter four on Quantock villages (see p. 58). Distance: about 12 miles. Map: ST 23/33.

> **Park in Cannington (GR ST255396) and take one of the unsignposted footpaths across the fields towards Blackmore. Cross the bypass – look left, then right, then left again – and continue across country until the path emerges onto Blackmore Lane (or Blackmoor as it is spelled at the other end – take your pick). In front of you is Blackmore Farm (GR ST245387).**

Blackmore Farm – referred to in the Domesday Book as Blachamore – is an old manor-house dating in its present form from the later half of the fifteenth century. It came shortly afterwards into the possession of Nicholas Halswell who married the daughter of the house. But the Halswells continued to base themselves at Halswell House, Goathurst – see later on this walk. It was bought by the present owners from the Miners' Pension Fund during the strike of 1984. It has a private chapel and wonderful oak-beamed ceilings in the bedrooms, in which, for a fee, you can sleep as a bed and breakfast guest of Ian and Anne Dyer. The medieval kitchen still has a lime ash floor and a great open fireplace.

> **The footpath continues past the farm buildings up the hill – turn right at the top – and leads shortly to Charlynch Church.**

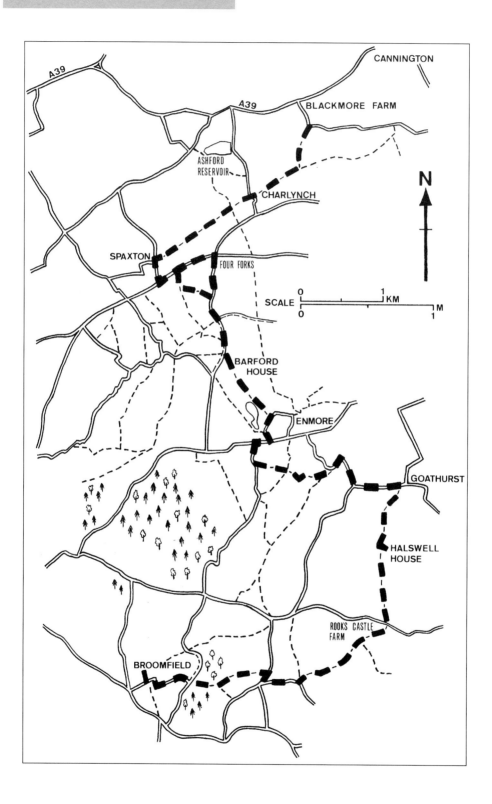

Charlynch Church. It is possible that a Saxon church stood on this site before the present building. (Charlynch is of Saxon derivation and means 'the terraced land of the churls'.) The south doorway, chancel arch, font and the remains of the north doorway date from the twelfth century. Most of the rest of the building is fourteenth century. There is an unusual feature at the top of the east window – the figures of four female saints: St Scytha holding keys, St Katharine with a sword and a book, St Apollonia holding pincers (she is the patron saint of dentists), and St Cecilia with a hand-organ. The church was treated to a typically Victorian over-restoration in 1868, but ceased to be an ecclesiastical building in 1988 when the altar and reredos were removed to nearby Spaxton church. It is currently undergoing conversion into a private dwelling.

> **Across the road from the church, the path plunges down the hill and passes through several fields towards Spaxton, its church tower visible for much of the way.**

The church of St Margaret and the nearby fifteenth-century Court Farm and mill are well worth a visit. More about these will be found under Spaxton (see p. 74).

> **On leaving the church by its east gate, turn right for a few yards and then walk up Splatt Lane to the T-junction with the village school almost opposite. Now turn left along the road for 100 yd and a public footpath signpost on the right indicates the way, cutting across fields to just above Barford House and Park.**
>
> **Alternatively, on reaching the T-junction in Spaxton, continue on the road for half a mile beyond the signpost to the crossroads at Four Forks with its garage, post office and shop. Here take the right-hand road signposted to Barford, and immediately you pass the now derelict chapel of the Agapemonite or Abode of Love religious colony founded in 1841 and closed in 1958. Continue on past the Lamb Inn and a mile further down the road is Barford House and Park.**

Barford House is an exquisite example of the smaller English country house. Queen Anne in design, the present frontage has no written history, and conceals a house older than the one announced

Opposite: Map 3. (Drawn by Jonathan White.)

Michael Stancomb at Barford Park. (Photograph by Chris Chapman.)

by its rosy eighteenth-century brickwork. It was rescued from imminent dereliction by Mr and Mrs Michael Stancombe in 1958 and was gradually restored to its present immaculate state. The gardens and park have also been reclaimed – with initial advice from garden designer Dame Sylvia Crowe – to form a perfect setting for the house. The house is open from 2 p.m. to 6 p.m. on Wednesdays, Thursdays and Bank Holiday weekends from May to September.

From the stable yard gate a footpath runs diagonally across the park of Barford House to Enmore Castle, a little under a mile away.

Enmore Castle is all that remains of a gigantic feudal folly built by the Earl of Egmont in the late eighteenth century. An ancient castle belonging to the Malet family – who once owned most of Somerset – was pulled down to make way for the new building. No planning laws in those days, no sentiment about heritage. But the monstrous size and complexity of the finished edifice – it had turrets and towers and extensive underground offices reached via a 40 ft dry moat – emptied the pockets of Egmont's less grandiose successors. Most of it was demolished, leaving the current rump standing and it is now divided into two houses. The public footpath crosses the lawn between the castle and its ornamental lake. There are fine views across the water to the south, made even more picturesque by Egmont's ruthless clearance of human and other intrusions into his private landscape. The castle now overlooks the 18 hole Enmore Park golf course. This 6,443 yd course is well wooded, with water features at five holes. Also close by is the parish church of St Michael with a Norman doorway and memorials to the Malet family.

Turn right onto the road through the village of Enmore, the church is on the left; the path crosses a field on the right and exits by a gate at the side of Enmore School.

Enmore School is famous as the first free elementary school in the country. It was built in 1810 by the Revd John Poole, cousin to Tom Poole of Nether Stowey, friend of the poets Coleridge and Wordsworth. If you are lucky you will see children in the playground doing dances that were recorded by the folk collector Cecil Sharpe on a visit to the village in 1910.

Take the road running south from the school and after 500 yd join the footpath on your left going to Andersfield Farm. Rejoin the road here and follow it to Goathurst, a mile away. At the edge of the village a road from the left comes up from the church 100 yd off, and on the right is the long driveway up to Halswell (pronounced Haswell) House.

'Ring-a-ring-o-Roses', Enmore School. (Photograph by Chris Chapman.)

35

Make a visit to the church of St Edward in Goathurst for it contains a splendid monument to Sir Nicholas Halswell, died 1633, with carved figures of him, his wife and nine children. The name Halswell is derived from 'hazel' and 'well'.

The footpath goes along the drive and then swings round to the right just before Halswell House is reached.

Halswell House. A yeoman's house once occupied this site – the Tudor buildings can still be seen to the rear of the seventeenth-century façade built after the style of Wren. The classical ruins that dot the landscape around the house are all that remain of one of the greatest 'undiscovered' gardens of the English landscape movement. When the façade was built, the ground at the front of the house had been laid out as a formal garden in the classical tradition, but in the middle of the eighteenth century this was erased by Sir Charles Kemeys Tynte in favour of a more 'natural' vista of meadows and trees. During the Second World War the house was taken over by the military and a prisoner-of-war camp for Italians built in the grounds. Pevsner wrote in 1958, 'At the time of writing unoccupied and not as well looked after as it would deserve.' Today the house is again occupied and undergoing some restoration.

Follow the path around the back of a copse that shelters the western side of the Halswell buildings – there are still signs of substantial deer fencing here. Along the edge of the wood at the top of the hill, the remains of the Robin Hood Hut, part of the ornate parkland plan, can be seen. Beyond Rooks Castle Farm, the path goes downhill again past Stream Farm, across the road and up through the woods to Fyne Court on the edge of Broomfield village.

Fyne Court. There is virtually nothing of the main house, which was burnt down in 1894, still standing. There are occasional events in the hall, the one building which survived the fire, and where Andrew Crosse conducted his electrical experiments in the middle of the nineteenth century. The Crosse estate of some 400 acres is now National Trust land with the buildings, a car park and 26 acres leased to the Somerset Wildlife Trust. There are pleasant walks through the grounds, and plants grown by the trust are on sale.

CHAPTER THREE

Plants and Wildlife

T he varied Quantock landscape makes for an interesting and varied flora and fauna. The main habitats are the farmland with its hedgerows and buildings, the moorland or heath with heathers, bracken and scattered storm-beaten trees, the broadleaved and conifer woodlands, the villages and parkland surrounding some of the big houses, and the freshwater springs, streams and ponds. The special coastal habitat has been dealt with in chapter one.

Farmland and Hedgerows

Perhaps the most important farmland feature for wildlife is the hedgerows. Where fields and lanes are bordered by earth banks topped with ancient hedges, there will be found a rich and diverse wildlife. Hedgerow butterflies are orange tips, meadow browns, gatekeepers, peacocks, small tortoiseshells, red admirals and there will also be myriads of other insects: moths, beetles, wasps, flies and bugs of all shapes and sizes.

The flowering of the hedgerows begins in spring, sometimes even in January, with primroses (*Primula vulgaris*), dog's mercury (*Mercurialis perennis*) and lesser celandines (*Ranunculus ficaria*) vying to be 'first out' (not counting winter heliotrope (*Petasites fragrans*) which is an interloper, a garden escape regretfully cropping up in far too many Somerset hedgerows to the detriment of the native flora). These are followed by cow parsley (*Anthriscus sylvestris*), stichwort (*Stellaria holostea*), bush vetch (*Vicia sepium*), herb Robert (*Geranium robertianum*), red campion (*Silene dioica*) and, in smaller amounts, shining cranesbill (*Geranium lucidum*). Since the authorities have been persuaded not to use herbicides along the verges of country lanes and the introduction of the Wildlife Act 1981 making it an offence to dig up wild plants, the wayside flora has greatly improved in recent years. Spraying takes place in

agricultural fields and pure seed mixtures have resulted in a decrease of many of the former cornfield weeds, but sometimes these do hang on in the corners of fields and the commoner weeds, such as field pansy (*Viola arvensis*), shepherd's purse (*Capsella bursa-pastoris*) and pineapple weed (*Matricaria matricariodes*), often occur in large numbers.

Of hedgerow shrubs, spindle (*Euonymus europaeus*), hazel (*Corylus avellana*) and blackthorn (*Prunus spinosa*) all flower early in the year followed by hawthorn (*Crataegus monogyna*), dog rose (*Rosa canina*), dogwood (*Cornus sanguinea*) and elder (*Sambucus nigra*). In winter the red twigs of the dogwood give colour to the hedges and are conspicuous even from a car. It is possible to estimate the age of a hedgerow by counting the number of woody species in a 30 yd stretch, and multiplying the number by 100. A hedge with only two such species will be 200 years old and one with eight species about 800 years. This may sound a rather rough guide, but where the age of hedgerows can be dated from documents, it has been found to be fairly accurate. A former picturesque feature of farmland, the majestic elm tree (*Ulmus procera*) has vanished due to the ravages of Dutch elm disease, which is spread by beetles, but there is plenty of elm still to be found in hedgerows and perhaps one day the saplings will again grow into the lofty trees where rooks loved to build their nests. At present they have to make do with trees at half the elm's height.

Food available around farms and farm buildings attracts many birds. In the winter there are sure to be chaffinches, starlings, greenfinches, blue and great tits, blackbirds, resident robins, house sparrows and wrens, and sometimes the pied wagtail running in the yards, and yellowhammer and bullfinches in the orchard. In the summer there is often quite a change-over, with swallows, house martins and spotted flycatchers taking over from the finches and tits who move away to nest in the nearby hedges and woods. The barn owl, once a familiar if ghostly sight around almost every farm where it fed largely on mice and voles, is now a rarity even on the Quantock farms.

Flocks of rooks, jackdaws, wood pigeons and starlings feed throughout the year in the fields, searching for insects, seeds and young shoots. They are often joined in the winter by lapwings, gulls, redwings and fieldfares. Goldfinches and linnets thrive on seeds of many wild flowers, especially thistle, docks and teasels.

The hedgerows, of course, are also important nesting sites for most of our common birds, blackbirds, chaffinches, robins, wrens,

Opposite: The authors stand by a pollarded oak in coppiced oak woodland, Holford Combe. (Photograph by Chris Chapman.)

bullfinches, thrushes and dunnocks and summer visitors like the blackcap and whitethroat. Small creatures too must not be overlooked: mice, voles, hedgehogs and snails rely on the hedgerows which are their highways with regular runs from homes in holes and crevices to feeding places. These can be traced by tell-tale piles of nutshells or seed husks left by mice or a stone surrounded by the shattered remains of snail shells denoting a thrush's anvil. On calm summer evenings, bats, usually pipistrelles and long-eared bats, may often be observed hunting for flies and moths along hedgerows and over farmland. The Daubenton's bat may sometimes be seen in daytime, flying over water.

Heathland

One of the most important habitats on the Quantocks is the moorland, technically known as coastal heath, as this comprises 12 per cent of the world's such habitat. It occupies the seaward end of the Quantock range, plus Aisholt Common.

This must be the most colourful of any of our native habitats in summer when the magenta bell heather (*Erica cinerea*) intermingles with yellow western gorse (*Ulex gallii*) to form a dense covering of solid colour. This heather is much brighter and longer lasting than the common ling (*Calluna vulgaris*) which also occurs, as does the taller, bush-forming common gorse (*Ulex europaeus*). Bristle bent grass (*Agrostis curtisii*) graduates through green to purple as the seasons advance and finally becomes a flaxen gold, unmistakable as it waves in the breeze. Wavy hair-grass (*Deschampsia flexuosa*) is also present but it turns a deeper golden colour and has more spreading flower-heads. Here and there is the occasional tree, mainly hawthorn or holly, windblown and nibbled into topiary shapes by grazing animals, the lowest twigs cropped by sheep. Above their reach the deer continue the artwork; how often they seem to achieve shapes resembling their own forms, ready to trick the unpractised deer-watcher into thinking they have a fine hind in their sights! Rowan (*Sorbus aucuparia*) and downy birch (*Betula pubescens*) trees are also common and both are important food sources for birds in autumn.

These open stretches, filled in summer with the scent of flowers and the humming of insects busy among the petals, are beloved by many of the migrant birds which travel thousands of miles to raise their young here. These include a few pairs of wheatears, tree pipits, whinchats and, more rarely, Britain's only migrant falcon, the hobby.

Richard Bolton, bee-keeper in Smith's Combe. (Photograph by Chris Chapman.)

There are also the native species which brave the elements all year round: stonechat, meadow pipit, skylark and kestrel, while buzzard quarter the open land searching for mice, voles and beetles.

An interesting nesting bird is the nightjar, which arrives in May from Africa to breed in Quantock combes. Flying and hunting moths by night, it can be heard at dusk when it begins its unmistakable churring 'song'. Sounding more like a stick being run along railings than a bird, it can keep this note up without seeming to draw breath. It also has a clear, liquid whistle, and can make a distinct clapping noise with its wings. By day they crouch unmoving on the ground where they are well camouflaged. The cuckoo is fairly common, with the meadow pipit being the usual foster parent on the moors, but they also frequently lay their eggs in the nests of tree pipits. Rare birds to the moorland include the red kite, hen harrier, and great grey shrike.

Stonechat and whinchat.
(Drawings by Jonathan White

Over-burning has been a serious threat to the heathland in the past, but this is now much more carefully controlled, but not before the spread of bracken had crowded out some moorland plants. A certain quantity of bracken is desirable for some invertebrates and to provide cover for deer, and also to give that glorious change of colour throughout the seasons: light green of young fronds, dark green in summer, yellowing suddenly at the first frosts and deepening through russet to a deep red after saturation by winter wet. However, a monoculture is not good for wildlife in general.

Those who care for the Quantocks are well aware of this and in 1993 a limited programme of spraying with Asulux, a selective weed-killer, took place and there are plans to continue this scheme. Attempts have also been made to cut the bracken and future years will show the effectiveness or otherwise of these methods. Another invasive plant is rhododendron (*Rhododendron ponticum*), splendid to look at in May in areas such as Staple Plain, but of little value to our ecology.

Beneath the colourful ground cover is a usually unseen, busy world. Lizards and, occasionally, the much maligned adder have their runs, also shrews scurry ever in search of food. The woolly caterpillars of fox moths, drinkers and oak eggar moths are fairly obvious when, after feeding on heathers and rushes, they make their way to pupate in the humus, often crossing tracks in the process. Most spectacular are the green-banded emperor moth larvae which also feed on heather. The adult moth has large false 'eyes' on its forewings and is very beautiful. Heathland butterflies include green hairstreak, small heath and grayling.

While on hands and knees inspecting these small wonders it will be noted that there are other flowers among the heather: tormentil (*Potentilla erecta*), heath bedstraw (*Galium saxatile*), heath milkwort (*Polygala serpyllifolia*) and heath spotted orchid (*Dactylorhiza maculata*). The Quantocks do not have the large areas of blanket bog which are found on Exmoor, but there are many damp spots and here may be found a good selection of bog plants, such as the third type of heather – cross-leaved heath (*Erica tetralix*), sometimes called bog heather – along with bog asphodel (*Narthecium ossifragum*), bog pimpernel (*Anagallis tenella*) and lousewort (*Pedicularis palustris*). There were some very exciting finds in 1993; cowberry (*Vaccinium vitis-idaea*), a relation of whortleberry with larger red fruits, was rediscovered after persistent searching by a team from the Somerset Atlas Flora project. The same team later on in the day found allseed (*Radiola linoides*) in its only known remaining Somerset site and chaffweed (*Anagallis minima*), a new record for the Quantocks; a memorable day for the botanists.

Some of the more open combes such as Weacombe are good places to seek the wild red deer which love to lie on the sheltered side of a valley. This, therefore, would seem an appropriate place to include some notes on this species.

The Wild Red Deer

At one time red deer died out on the Quantocks and were reintroduced from the Exmoor herd in 1860 by Fenwick Bisset of Bagborough House. For some years about fifteen deer were trapped

Red deer: stag, hind and calf.
Photograph by David Doble.)

annually and brought over to the woods, and although some soon made their way back to Exmoor, sufficient stayed to breed and build up a Quantock herd. Regular hunting of the deer started in 1920 by the Quantock Staghounds. Hunting takes place two or three times each week during the season which starts in August and goes on until the end of April.

Only the Red deer stags grow antlers, which are shed from late March to early May. New growth starts at once and by mid-August the fresh antlers will be fully developed. Calves are born mainly in June and for the first few days lie under cover in heather, whortleberry and by woodland edges. The mother is always nearby and returns every four or five hours for the calf to take a feed of milk. Should anyone come across a deer calf, remember it has not been abandoned by its mother, and must not be picked up.

For many years a white hind named Snowy by the local people was a much loved, familiar sight in the Bagborough area and was never hunted. She was pure white apart from a few brown patches. Unfortunately in February 1993, when nineteen years old, she was killed by poachers, probably run down by dogs. Her remains were found at the foot of Bagborough Park. There was a public outcry and the sad news was reported in many of the national daily newspapers. Another red deer 'personality' is a stag which has deserted the herd and taken up residence with some cows near Bicknoller and he spends his day grazing with them in a grass field. Perhaps he thinks he is a cow or else he has just opted for an easy life!

These days the deer are accustomed to seeing people walking the hills, and often they will remain quite motionless on an upper slope while humans traverse a path below them. If you stay on the path and keep moving as if you had not spotted them, they will be content to watch you go by. However, if you stand and stare or leave the path to try to approach too near, they will quickly bound away.

Small numbers of roe deer have moved into the Quantock woods in recent years. They are only about half the size of red deer, and their white rump patch, with no visible tail, is a good identification point.

Deciduous Woodland

The upper reaches of Holford and Hodder's Combes are clothed in sessile oak woods, last coppiced about 100 years ago for the tanning industry. Beneath these trees and around Dowsborough Hill Fort, the ground is covered with whortleberry shrubs, which once seen in spring with the sunlight glinting on their pink-tipped leaves creating a mystic beauty, will never be forgotten. The leaves grow larger here in the shade of woodland than on the open moorland, and so do the fruits, but there are fewer berries and 'wort gatherers' usually congregate in the moorland combes.

In many broad-leaved woodlands the familiar flowers such as the dainty trefoil-leaved wood sorrel (*Oxalis acetosella*), bluebells (*Hyacinthoides non-scripta*) and wood anemones (*Anemone nemorosa*) occur, but it is harder to find meadow saffron (*Colchicum autumnale*), a Quantock 'special'. It has pink crocus-like flowers which bloom in autumn.

One needs to rise early (about 4 a.m.) to appreciate the full impact of the dawn chorus of woodland birds when in May the residents are joined by summer visitors. Blackcap, willow warbler, chiffchaff, wood warbler, pied flycatcher, redstart, and cuckoo are the chief visitors, and the residents include blackbird, song thrush, robin and a variety of tits. All these join in the dawn chorus which may be interspersed with the raucous cry of a jay and perhaps a hooting tawny owl returning home after a night hunting. The long-eared owl has nested in the oak woodland in recent years. Nuthatches, tree creepers and green and great spotted woodpeckers also frequent the woods, and may be seen clinging close to a tree-trunk as they work their way up, collecting insects from the crevices in the bark.

Grey squirrels and wood mice are busy in their search for nuts and acorns, but busiest of all perhaps are the wood ants as they struggle along bearing pieces of leaf debris several times their own length with which to build their nests which are common in the woods. The nests are usually about 18 in high but quite often reach 3 ft or more and may contain as many as 200,000 ants.

Badgers, too, are old inhabitants of these woodlands, seldom seen by day but their sets, usually with several entrances (or exit) holes may be found, distinguished from a large rabbit or fox hole by the debris of bedding dragged out by brock to air. He likes a frequent change and carries the dried grass in a bundle tucked under his chin and shuttles backwards with it into the set. They are very particular animals and their latrines will also be found nearby, but away from the set and where they feed.

Coniferous Woodland

The present area of approximately 3,000 acres known as Quantock Forest consists of Forestry Commission plantations of mainly conifers which have been grown since about 1920. Before that the

Martin Ebsary and sons, Paul and Andrew, foresters on Lord's Ball. (Photograph by Chris Chapman.)

area was oak woodland as already described, but this was felled during and just after the First World War. Trees planted include large stands of Douglas fir and Sitka spruce, with smaller amounts of Scots pine, Japanese and European larch, Norway spruce, Western hemlock, Grand fir, Western red cedar, and Corsican pine together with a few other species of conifer and some broad-leaved trees.

Although the original wartime felling must have created havoc with the wildlife, the subsequent conifer forests today give us a contrasting habitat. Grey squirrels build their leafy treetop dreys which are lined with grass; red deer frequently harbour here. Ground flora is sparse or non-existent in the darkness below a plantation of firs or pines but it is a good hunting ground for fungi after autumn rain, including the well-known red and white fly agaric, some of the colourful species of russula and various milk-caps which exude a milk-like fluid when broken. Larch bolete may be found where the host tree grows. There are many smaller species too such as *Calocera viscosa* which has yellow, branched stems.

Birds which are attracted to these dark surroundings, feeding on seeds from the cones or insects attracted by the resinous aroma, include parties of tits, goldcrests, crossbills, redpolls and, since

1980, siskins. Buzzards and sparrow hawks nest in the tops of some of the taller trees, as do wood pigeons, jays and turtle doves.

Butterflies are not much attracted to conifers but are sometimes seen in the wide forest tracks where flowers grow as the sun streams in. More likely to be seen are the conifer feeding moths such as *Dioryctria abietella* which are resident, but numbers may be swelled by migrants in some seasons. Here again may be found wood ant nests; these insects seem not to mind whether they dwell in deciduous or coniferous woodland. This is rather unusual as most insects are dependent on one particular plant or habitat, but the wood ant has a varied diet of insects and vegetable matter.

Villages and Parkland

Areas surrounding habitations, although not strictly wild, none the less attract certain plants and animals which have now become associated with man or his buildings. The well-dug soil of gardens proves suitable for all those annual weeds so familiar to horticulturalists: dandelions, groundsels, speedwells, spurges, bittercress and conversely, former garden plants have spread into nearby hedgerows where snowdrops, winter heliotrope and hybrid bluebells appear. Many plants formerly grown for their medicinal and herbal uses still linger around villages: comfrey (*Symphytum officinale*), feverfew (*Tanacetum parthenium*), yarrow (*Achillea*

oyce and Tom Bushen,
Halsway Nursery. (Photograph
by Chris Chapman.)

millefolium), coltsfoot (*Tussilago farfaro*) and greater celandine (*Chelidonium majus*) fall within this category. They were once used in the manufacture of cough mixtures, decoctions, poultices and ointments to cure all manner of ills, and coltsfoot was even dried and used as a substitute for tobacco.

Garden birds will be familiar to anyone who puts out food for them in the winter, an essential part of their diet, so keep feeding them! Almost everyone can name robin, blackbird, blue tit, house sparrow, starling and collared dove, although the latter only arrived in England in 1955 and on the Quantocks in 1964. Tender lettuces and seedlings attract slugs and snails which are pursued by song thrushes, and the ready supply of food provided by householders encourages some of the smaller birds to nest nearby.

One may wonder where house martins built before we provided houses with sheltering eaves (presumably on cliff faces), and in 1993 swallows nested in the porch of Stringston church. This churchyard is unusual also in having a juniper tree planted instead of the usual yew. Over Stowey churchyard is the place to visit for spring flowers with very early-flowering lesser celandines (*Ranunculus ficaria*), and primroses (*Primula vulgaris*). These are followed in March by masses of wild daffodils (*Narcissus pseudonarcissus*), well worth the drive there to see them. If you are interested in snowdrops, Kilve churchyard is the place to visit in February where there are several different introduced species.

Churchyards are so frequently good hunting grounds for botanists as they often represent the last remaining area of natural grassland in a village. The vicar of Aisholt has realized this and made the sloping ground around the church into a nature reserve; there is a water-colour in the porch showing some of the flowers which grow there. Churches themselves also provide nesting and roosting places for birds such as swifts, jackdaws and owls, and the belfries may shelter pipistrelle and other species of bats.

In the old days almost all the big houses were surrounded by parkland, stocked mainly with fallow deer. Then it was considered that 'A park without deer is like a room without paintings.' Domestic deer have now disappeared, but much of the parkland remains at places like Crowcombe Court, Bagborough House and St Audries, West Quantoxhead. The grass here is now shared by cattle, sheep and the wild deer who leap with the greatest of ease over a 6 foot fence.

Rabbits, and sometimes hare, graze and frolic beneath fine specimens of English oak (*Quercus robur*), chestnut (*Castanea*

isholt conservation
nurchyard. (Photograph by
hris Chapman.)

sativa) and beech (*Fagus sylvatica*) trees. The Holford Beeches are a row of particularly fine specimens on the hill behind Alfoxden. A rough estimate of the age of a tree can be made by measuring the girth of the trunk about 5 ft from the ground and converting the inches to years. So a girth of 10 ft means the tree is about 120 years old. Many of the trees are older than this for they were planted two or even three hundred years ago. Note the typical shape of parkland trees which have all the lower twigs on a level, horizontal plane, the result of animals nibbling them over the years. The height of the lowest twigs above ground shows the height to which the tallest animals can reach.

Freshwater Habitats

There remains one important habitat to review: the freshwater areas. No major rivers rise on the Quantocks but a number of streams, which on Exmoor would be termed 'waters' but on the Quantocks are often called 'brooks', have their source in boggy moorland springs. At Holford, two streams converge, one rising near Bicknoller Post and flowing via Hodder's Combe and the other running below Dowsborough through Holford Combe. From Holford the combined waters flow past Kilve to the sea. Cannington Brook receives the waters from Rams Combe, Quantock Combe and Cockercombe after they have passed through Hawkridge Reservoir and the smaller Ashford Reservoir, and then drains into the River Parrett. The west boundary of Quantock is marked by the Doniford Stream, which reaches the sea at Doniford, near Watchet. Its headwaters are near Triscombe and all the valley combes on this side of the Quantocks drain into it.

Special birds on the streams include the dipper, grey wagtail and heron. Hemlock water dropwort (*Oenothera crocata*), cuckooflower (*Cardamine pratensis*), yellow iris (*Iris pseudacorus*) and marsh marigold (*Caltha palustris*) are among the flowering plants.

The moorland springs contain many interesting plants. Sphagnum mosses form a spongy bed making a suitable habitat for sedges and rushes of many varieties together with moorland crowfoot (*Ranunculus omiophyllus*), bog stitchwort (*Stellaria alsine*) and marsh pennywort (*Hydrocotyle vulgaris*).

Reservoirs and Ponds

None of the brooks are of a size to attract trout fishermen, so familiar on Exmoor waters, but there is good fishing to be had at Hawkridge Reservoir. This was stocked with rainbow trout in 1962 and is a popular place for competitions, particularly at weekends. There are also plenty of rudd. Coming down to young jamjar fishermen there are sticklebacks, eels and smooth newts, toad and frog tadpoles and many a water beetle, snails and other invertebrates.

Hawkridge Reservoir also provides a feeding area for water fowl with wintering numbers of tufted duck, pochard, mallard, coot, moorhen, Canada geese, heron, little grebe and great-crested grebe. The last mentioned also breeds here and it is a charming sight to see the proud parent grebes with their young in spring, the chicks often being carried on the back of a parent. There are many fascinating plants which grow on the banks of the reservoir. Orange foxtail grass (*Alopecurus aequalis*), water chickweed (*Myosoton aquaticum*), marsh yellowcress (*Rorippa palustris*), red goosefoot (*Chenopodium rubrum*), round-fruited rush (*Juncus compressus*), trifid bur-marigold (*Bidens tripartita*), water forget-me-not (*Myosotis scorpioides*) and amphibious bistort (*Polygonum amphibium*) have all been seen in recent years. In the water there is spiked water milfoil (*Myriophyllum spicatus*) and horned pondweed (*Zannichellia palustris*).

Other ponds and pools, man-made or otherwise, provide interest. Wilmot's Pool on the moor above Crowcombe Park Gate is a suitable spawning ground for frogs and newts and is much used as a drinking pool by the Quantock ponies. Floating club-rush (*Eleogiton fluitans*) is an unusual grass-like plant which has been found there. Moorhens and mallard nest by the village ponds at East Quantoxhead and Dodington. Yellow iris (*Iris pseudacorus*) is frequently found in old farm ponds, mill pools and ornamental ponds, all of which have a measure of freshwater life.

Non-flowering Plants

Fungi, mosses, liverworts and lichens, all of which need a degree of specialized knowledge to name them correctly, proliferate in the clean Quantock atmosphere. Each separate habitat has its own particular associated species, some of which grow on the ground and others on shrubs and trees.

In shady areas there are many ferns: broad buckler (*Dryopteris dilatata*), scaly male-fern (*D. affinis*), soft shield-fern (*Polystichum setiferum*), lady fern (*Athyrium felix-femina*) and hartstongue (*Asplenium scolopendrium*) are common. Hard fern (*Blechnum spicant*), which is distinguished by its two different types of fronds, a rosette of sterile ones at the base with taller, spore-bearing fronds growing from the centre, is found on acid ground, and several small species of spleenwort bedeck walls and banks. Hay-scented buckler-fern (*Dryopteris aemula*) is more unusual but can be found in profusion in at least one moorland combe.

The diversity and variety of wildlife on the Quantocks offers much enjoyment for the visiting naturalist, whether young or old, a beginner or someone with years of experience. In fact, the more one knows, the greater the enjoyment and the greater the possibility of making new and worthwhile discoveries.

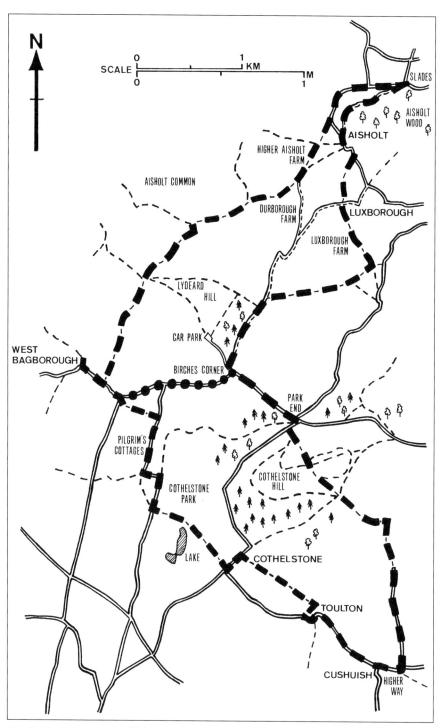

Map 4. (Drawn by Jonathan White.)

West Bagborough–Aisholt–Cothelstone

This walk links the villages of West Bagborough, Aisholt and Cothelstone and passes through lanes and tracks over moorland, farmland and woodland with superb viewpoints on both Lydeard and Cothelstone Hill. The route is via West Bagborough, Lydeard Hill, Durborough Farm, Aisholt Wood, Aisholt, Luxborough Farm, Ralph's Copse, Birches Corner, Park End, Cothelstone, Cothelstone Park, Pilgrims Cottages and returns to West Bagborough. Distance: about 12 miles. Map: ST 03/13.

> **From West Bagborough take the track on the left of the Rising Sun Inn (GR ST170334) which leads up on to Lydeard Hill.**

West Bagborough. Bagborough House near the church is a Georgian building with an attractive colonnade of five bays. In the middle of the nineteenth century this was the home of Fenwick Bisset, renowned among the masters of staghounds for in 1860 he began to re-establish the red deer on the Quantock Hills.

> **On Lydeard Hill (1,197 ft) cross over the ridge and follow the footpath down into the valley to Durborough Farm and on to Higher Aisholt Farm. Stay on the high road above the valley. At Slades (GR ST198362) take the track on your left down into Aisholt Wood.**

Aisholt Wood (the name refers to ash trees) is managed by the Somerset Wildlife Trust and in spring is a sea of bluebells. Red deer harbour here.

> **When you reach the road turn left and walk up the hill to Aisholt Church.**

Aisholt churchyard is everything a country churchyard should be. A scheme instigated by a local farmer keeps the lawnmower at bay until the flowering season is over. In late spring it is a delight with primroses, ramsons, lords-and-ladies (wild arum) and early purple orchid, to name but a few.

Inside the church of All Saints are some good points of interest. To the left of the door you will find an old chest carved out of a solid oak log. Being extremely heavy, it was at one time used for safeguarding the church valuables. It has three locks, a separate key being held by the parson and two churchwardens, and was the Christian solution to exercising trust!

At the top of the south aisle is a chantry chapel and from there you can see a large opening in the wall giving a view through to the chancel's altar. Referred to as a hagioscope (holy view), it is more commonly known as a squint, and is likely to have been for the benefit of the congregation seated in the chapel as well as for the chantry priest.

Walk out of the churchyard by the top gate and along the road in a southerly direction passing the old thatched schoolhouse where Henry Newbolt, the poet and writer, lived in the 1930s. When you reach a cottage on your right, go down the track and immediately after the second cottage follow the path through the fields to Luxborough. Take the track down towards Luxborough Farm and as the road bends to the right, climb over the stile and cross over the valley to the start of what was once a green lane to Birches Corner (GR ST182336).

It is suggested you walk this route because at one time it must have been beautiful and is a lesson in how landscape can quickly change. As we write this the bottom end of Ralph's Copse has been felled. There are mature beech trees and it may well be that the owner intends to replant. Crossing the valley bottom is not easy but possible. At the top of the hill on the other side you will reach a hedge and a track from the road. The OS map will now confuse you. At one time a green lane ran up the hill and joined the track to Birches Corner but all the hedges that divided the fields as shown on the map have been grubbed out. Stay by the remaining hedge and walk uphill in a westerly direction. There is a tiny remnant of beech hedge and lane at the top.

(Frank and Jack Clatworthy. Wildlife Photographers. Photograph by Chris Chapman.)

At Birches Corner turn left and walk down the road to Park End, turn right and almost immediately follow the steep path on your left up onto Cothelstone Hill.

Cothelstone Hill commands fine views to the south and has an attractive group of beech trees known as Cothelstone Clump. Like many other summits on the Quantocks, it has a Bronze Age cairn, but there are also the foundation walls of a round tower that served as a lookout for spotting fire beacons in times of national danger. Somerset County Council has also a small herd of Exmoor ponies grazing on the hill, an oddity to some when there are already Quantock ponies at large. At the south-east corner of the open hill the wardens have built a holding pen so that the herd can be rounded up for periodic checks. A few years ago the hill was densely bracken covered but the Quantock wardens have organized biennial cutting to produce the pleasant open area we see today where eyebright, bird's-foot trefoil and bedstraws nestle in the turf. The curious plant growing around the ruined tower is Good King Henry (*Chenopodium bonus-henricus*). Yellow-hammers, stonechats, linnets and other birds nest here and ringlet butterflies occur.

Near the summit of the hill where the paths cross, keep straight on and walk off the open hill at the south-east corner. Follow the path through the edge of the woods keeping the fields on your right. At GR ST198322 turn sharp right and drop off the hills via the green lane to Higher Way and Cushuish. Walk in a northwesterly direction to Toulton and either walk through the fields past the Lawns (Old Kennels) to Cothelstone or take the road.

Cothelstone. Before visiting the church, walk up the road past the farm and village hall. On your left a small gate takes you into a field. Turn immediately right and you will find St Agnes Well almost buried in a sea of horsetails. This is a dipping well taken from a small spring that rises above Badger Copse. On your way back glance over the wall at the farm buildings. The arches under the nineteenth-century barn are supported by what appear to be Norman pillars, and are similar in design to the ones found in the Norman church of Stogursey.

The path follows the drive under the gate arch to Cothelstone Manor and then bears left to the church passing a row of cottages.

Cothelstone Manor has had a turbulent history. Sir John Stawell was a Royalist and during the Civil War of the 1640s he suffered severe punishment at the hands of the Parliamentarians. They half wrecked the manor and imprisoned him at Newgate. His son, another Sir John Stawell who was firmly loyal to King James, voiced his disgust at Judge Jeffreys' inhumanity to the supporters of the Monmouth rebellion of 1685. By way of reply Jeffreys hanged two rebels, Thomas Blackmore and Col. Bovett, from the gate to the manor. It is hard not to conjure up their swinging bodies as you walk under the arch.

The church of St Thomas of Canterbury is well worth a visit. It has a Norman pillar of different girth to those of the farmyard, and a squint that looks over the effigies of Sir Matthew Stalwell and Eleanor de Merton, his feet resting on a lion and hers on a pair of squirrels. Outside in the graveyard where a fine copper beech tree grows, can be found the tomb of Ianthe, daughter of the poet Shelley, who married an Esdaile and lived at the manor.

Follow the track north-west which runs from opposite the church gate through Cothelstone Park, the first part of which is farmland. Cross the brook with its pink blossoms of great willowherb, along with white hemlock, water dropwort and blue brooklime, and make for the line of Lombardy poplars. Keep the lake on your left and note the fine old English oaks on the crest of the hill. When you reach the road bear right.

After walking up the lane for about 200 yd you will notice a small cast-iron bridge spanning the road. There are substantial buildings here dating from 1818 that were once associated with a fine mansion called Cothelstone House. It was demolished in the 1960s. The bridge connected the house and grounds with a walled garden. The lane turns sharp left, then a right-hand turn passes Pilgrims Cottages where a rusty galvanized iron roof covers the original thatch.

After about a quarter of a mile take the path on your left opposite a bungalow. This runs across the fields back to West Bagborough.

Note: This walk can be divided into two parts of about 6 miles each by using the road which runs from Birches Corner to West Bagborough.

CHAPTER FOUR

Quantock Villages

M any of the towns and cities in Britain began as little more than villages and outgrew their rural roots to meet the demands of industry and commerce. Not that villages were without industry: the blacksmith not only shod horses and oxen up to the middle of the nineteenth century but also made the tools used on the farm, the wheelwright built the carts and hay waggons, the mason, carpenter and thatcher built the cottages, the miller in the local water-mill ground the corn that the village baker turned into bread, and the innkeeper brewed the beer and cider he sold. Village craftsmen and the women provided for almost all the needs of their communities, and the chapman tramping from hamlet to farmhouse with his wicker basket supplied such necessities as cottons, buttons, needles and elastic. With slowly changing tastes, some increase in affluence and dwindling populations, many small-scale village industries slowly faded away.

The church is most likely to be the oldest building in a Quantock village today, and the monuments and inscribed tablets tell the story of generations passed. Perhaps the great charm of the villages lies in the fact that they were rarely planned but grew up around the church, inn and school. For centuries agriculture and its needs was the life-blood of the economy, and to a certain extent it still is, though far fewer folk are now employed on the land. With housewives travelling a dozen miles to a supermarket, most village shops have closed, and some are struggling to keep their post offices open. In some places today there is more likely to be a potter selling his handmade wares to tourists, or a nursery offering a wide range of plants. Crowcombe, Enmore, Nether Stowey and Spaxton still have their primary schools and here mothers can still meet for a daily chatter. Otherwise, apart from the church, the inn which remains in almost every village is often the longest surviving institution.

People who recall with great pleasure happy holidays spent in Quantock country often retire to a favourite village here. They come with fresh ideas and support for church and chapel and a wide range of local activities, and soon become an essential part of the

est Somerset Morris Men,
alsway Manor. (Photograph
Chris Chapman.)

community. Homes often have fresh names: Old School House, Old Rectory, Old Bakery, Old Forge, Old Mill House, and at Holford the Combe House Hotel was once an old tannery, and Alfoxton Park Hotel a stately home. All indicative of changing village life.

*****

Please note: the following descriptions of the Quantock villages are arranged in alphabetical order but see Chapter One for East Quantoxhead, Kilve and Lilstock.

Aisholt (GR ST195356)

Aisholt lies in a deep hollow under the slopes of Middle Hill, its grey church tower and pink cottages peeping out above the clustering trees. The hedgerows bordering the narrow road winding down into the village are full of dogwood, spindle, holly and hawthorn, all indicating that this is an ancient way. The name Aisholt, usually spelt without the second vowel in the last century, means Ash Copse, still a common tree in many Quantock valleys. Coleridge was on friendly terms with the rector, John Brice, and thought at one time of living at Aisholt which he described as 'that green, romantic chasm'. The plan was dropped as his wife Sara thought it too isolated and he wrote to Tom Poole, 'Sara being Sara, and I being I, we must live in a town or close to one, so that she may have neighbours and acquaintances.' In 1800 there were 30 houses

Old Schoolhouse, Aisholt.
(Photograph by Lesley
Thomas.)

and 130 inhabitants, and it is no bigger today and still remains delightfully remote.

A writer and poet who did come to dwell in Aisholt in the thatched Old School House below the church was Sir Henry Newbolt, 1862–1938, and his wife Margaret. He is best remembered for his spirited sea songs 'Drake's Drum' and 'The Quarter-Gunner's Yarn', and especially locally for 'A Song of Exmoor' and 'April on Waggon Hill'. Henry Newbolt had a deep affection for Aisholt, its peace and wildlife, and he wrote in a letter to a friend:

How I hope that no one will ever spread its fame. As I brushed my snowy hair this morning, I cast an eye out of my window, and saw a moorhen walking, just like Aunt Julia, past our gate and up the road towards the well where the dipper is usually seen (he's singing at this moment) and where the kingfishers daily conduct their kinglets from the pond across by our hedge to the brook, and where we yesterday saw four goldcrests in the cherry tree. Let no one hear of it while the moon endureth.

We are sure that both Coleridge and Newbolt would be delighted to discover that today the churchyard at Aisholt is now a conservation area where the wild creatures and flowers get special protection. A painting showing some of the flowers hangs in the church porch where swallows also nest, a little matter noted by the rural dean during a visit in 1840. The church of All Saints is mainly fourteenth century and is full of interest: an ancient south door and roof to nave and aisle, a huge hagioscope piercing the chancel wall to give a view to the altar, an oak chest 800 years old, a hatchment of Charles Cross of Plainsfield painted on slate, and the parish tithe map. There is a car park just above the church.

Bicknoller (GR ST111395)

Here old thatched cottages mingle with modern houses and bungalows in one of Quantock's prettiest villages. Tiny streams, half hidden by wild flowers, ferns and grasses, run alongside the narrow roads and pass the Bicknoller Inn, called the New Inn in 1890. Off from the main road, and with no way over the hills except by foot up Bicknoller Combe, it is a tranquil place today. A hundred years ago it was much noisier when the big stone quarry was working on the edge of the village, and the inhabitants included a blacksmith, mason and wheelwright, thatcher, and Joel Jennings the postmaster who doubled as a carpenter. There was a school as well, built in 1864 with thirty pupils, but this closed in 1938 and the only tradesman left was a shopkeeper. Bicknoller probably began as a Saxon settlement and in 1086 had 13 villagers, 4 smallholders and 4 slaves. The stock included 2 horses, 4 cattle, 6 pigs and 80 sheep.

The fine fifteenth-century red sandstone church is dedicated to St George, and 200 years ago Collinson, the county historian, wrote: 'In the churchyard there is a fine old cross, and a very large aged yew tree.' Both are still there, the 12½ ft high cross on an octagonal base of three steps is a hundred years older than the church. The yew tree is probably 400 years old and now shelters the village stocks. In one corner of the churchyard is the village pound, and nearby a line of seven tombstones of the Bickham family. At one time they kept greyhounds, and frustrated when the wind was in the wrong direction for coursing, they would shoot at the weathercock on the tower to turn it round leaving holes which are still visible.

Cottages at Bicknoller.
(Photograph by Lesley
Thomas.)

A young yew tree took root on the tower and was 5 ft high in 1893 but has now disappeared, although in 1932 it was carved on a bench end within the church. There is some fine stone tracery in the chancel windows, and five carved beasts round the tower which is also adorned with some rather grotesque gargoyles along the roof. The fan-vaulted oak screen is one of seven carved for churches around Dunster just after 1495, and many of the bench ends with flower and leaf designs were added shortly afterwards. Here, as in much of West Somerset, the church is the oldest and most interesting feature of this delightful village. Thorncombe with its old house, and Paradise Farm and Combe are part of the parish. The impressive Halsway Manor, lying half-way between Bicknoller and Crowcombe, is now a folk centre with a variety of residential courses on folklore, dancing and singing. The name no doubt comes from 'hazel', a common and useful tree of the district.

Broomfield (GR ST224321)

This somewhat scattered village lies high on the south end of the Quantock ridge, and is reached by a variety of narrow, winding beech-lined roads. There is an interesting church, a patch of grass grandly known as The Green, and a few big houses and cottages all well spread out and surrounded by fields and hedgerows. Four hundred acres of common land is now mainly scrub with patches of broom from which the parish is named. In addition to the church the chief interest is Fyne Court, once the home of Andrew Crosse, 1784–1855, an early pioneer into atmospheric electricity. One of his experiments required the stringing up of 600 yd of copper wire on trees and poles to attract and conduct electricity to apparatus in his laboratory. The sparks and flashes caused by his work led him to be known locally as the 'Thunder and Lightning Man'. The main house was burnt down in 1894, and what survived is now the headquarters of the Somerset Wildlife Trust. Fyne Court is well signposted, and has a car park, picnic area, interpretation centre about the work of the trust, and a shop. The old Crosse estate of 400 acres now belongs to the National Trust, with the buildings and 26 acres leased to the Somerset Wildlife Trust.

The church of Saint Mary and All Saints is largely fifteenth century but with some rebuilding over the past 200 years. The best things in the church are the fine bench ends, one bearing the name of Simon Werman which also appears at Trull (but spelt 'Warman') with the inscription, 'Simon Warman maker of thys worke 1560'. A small table near the south door with a band of copper across it was once used by Andrew Crosse in his laboratory. A memorial obelisk, some 15 ft high, stands in the churchyard with an inscription by his wife Cornelia, 'Sacred to the memory of Andrew Crosse, The Electrician. He was humble towards God and kind to his fellow creatures.' By all accounts a true reflection on a remarkable man who spent much of his life in this upland Quantock village. An interesting feature on the north wall of the churchyard is a number of small stone tablets bearing such letters and figures as, 'ED 9 foot', 'SCT 18 foot', and 'HT 9 foot'. These stipulate various sections of the wall that certain householders were expected to maintain in the old days.

Cothelstone (GR ST182318)

This is a gem among Quantock villages, though a tiny one, for apart from a few scattered farms and cottages, there is just the historic manor-house, its farm buildings, and the adjacent church dedicated to St Thomas of Canterbury. A much larger house known as Cothelstone House was erected half a mile away in 1818 by Charles Esdaile who acquired the manor in 1793. His son Edward married Ianthe, daughter of the poet Shelley, and her tombstone stands in the churchyard here. Cothelstone House was demolished in the 1960s and the Esdaile descendants have returned to live in the old manor-house. A well, with an old stone head, in a nearby field once supplied water to the house and has long been known as St Agnes Well. This was once a favourite resort of maidens seeking a husband especially on St Agnes eve, 29 January.

During the Civil War, Sir John Stawell of Cothelstone Manor was a loyal follower of King Charles I, and as Cromwell's New Model Army took over much of Somerset during 1645, the manor-house was attacked and partially destroyed. Sir John was taken prisoner at the siege of Exeter, and his refusal to cooperate with the sequestrators led to the sale of all his property for £64,000 and his imprisonment in Newgate. He survived for the return of Charles II and the restoration of his estate but died shortly after. Twenty years later another Sir John Stawell refused to receive the monstrous Judge Jeffreys. He responded in his usual cruel fashion by ordering the hanging of two Monmouth rebels, Thomas Blackmore and Col. Bovett, on the outer gateway to the manor-house.

The way to the church passes under the stone archway of the gate, then along the main drive, and just before the house is reached it turns to the left and winds past a couple of cottages. The church tower is seen rising above the manor-house which has its own sixteenth-century gatehouse adorned with stone balusters and shell alcoves. Inside the church are some effigies of the Stawell family in the south chapel including fourteenth-century stone figures of Sir Matthew Stawell and his wife Elizabeth with her feet resting on two squirrels and two angels at the head. They had fourteen sons and seven daughters. There are two fine alabaster effigies of Sir John Stawell, died 1603, with his hand resting on a book, and of his wife, Frances. Also in the chapel, which is the oldest part of the building and dates from around 1200, is a wall memorial to the Royalist, Sir John Stawell, who died in 1661.

Cothelstone is a delightful, tranquil corner of the Quantock countryside, with its church, manor-house, cottages, the lover's well, wooded hillsides to the skyline, and a host of memories.

Crowcombe (GR ST140367)

Thomas Gerard writing in 1633 says, 'Crowcombe seated under Quantock hills which whether it took that name from crowes or noe, I know not'. In Domesday Book of 1087 it is written Crawecumbe, and most etymologists agree that old Thomas Gerard got the meaning right.

Church of the Holy Ghost, Crowcombe. (Photograph by Lesley Thomas.)

Today the village stretches for almost a mile with buildings old and new on both sides of the street. Until a bypass was constructed in 1919 this was part of the 1807 Minehead to Taunton turnpike road. The village shop closed in 1993 but the post office survives, and opposite, a footpath runs up through fields and the woodland edge to Crowcombe Park Gate and on to open moorland. This gate should not be confused with Crowcombe Combe Gate on the road that goes up the valley to Dead Woman's Ditch and then divides for Nether Stowey or Holford. Beyond the post office in Crowcombe is the Carew Arms, a seventeenth-century inn and close by on a triangle of grass stands a thirteenth-century cross marking the site of an ancient market and fair. Near the centre of the village is the parish

Church of the Holy Ghost, an unusual dedication, beautifully set amid giant oaks and against a background of hanging woods climbing 600 ft up the hillside.

The red sandstone fourteenth-century church tower had a spire 80 foot tall until it was struck by lightning and crashed down in 1725. The top section stands in the churchyard. There is some fine fan tracery in the porch ceiling which has a room above that was probably used by the priest in the early days, and later for a schoolroom. Inside, the south aisle is impressive, and the early fifteenth-century sculptured font and the fascinating carved bench ends with a variety of figures and foliage should not be missed. One is dated 1534 and another shows a man fighting a dragon. The chancel screen erected in 1729 with the pulpit and altar are the work of Thomas Parker the chief architect of Crowcombe Court. On the north side of the nave is the raised manor chapel completed in 1665 by Thomas Carew for his family at Crowcombe Court. Hatchments belonging to the Carews decorate the walls of the chapel. Crowcombe Court stands at the end of a long drive above the church and is an imposing red-brick mansion with a fine Georgian façade and a large stable block. Included is a mounting block incorporating a dog kennel. The main house today is a residential home.

Just below the church is the old Church House, a long stone building with a most interesting history. It dates from 1515 and at first it was used for parish festivals and functions and was where ale was brewed and money raised for church and local funds. Later an upper floor was added and in 1668 this became the village school, used until the present school was built in 1872. In 1668 Elizabeth Carew left £200 to the parish and this was laid out to buy 33 acres of land in nearby Bishop's Lydeard. The rent was sufficient to teach fifteen poor boys 'to read, write and cast sums, the boys to have annually a suit of plain clothes' and the balance of the rent constituted the master's salary. The ground floor of Church House accommodated the village poor until they were moved to the dreaded workhouse in Williton, erected in 1837. Eventually, the Church House came into the hands of two separate owners and there is a story related by Richard Jeffries in his book *Field and Hedgerow*, 'It came about that the roof decayed and the upper owner suggested to the lower owner that they should agree to bearing the cost of repair. Upon which the owner of the basement remarked that he contemplated pulling his part down.' By 1907 the building was stated to be 'quite ruinous', but an appeal raised £550 for the necessary repairs and it now has a magnificent timber roof. Again it

Church House, Crowcombe.
(Drawing by Jonathan White.)

is back to its original community use, the lower part as a village hall, the upper has regular craft and art exhibitions and is open throughout the summer. Adjoining the Church House is the old village pound and behind is the modern equivalent – a car park.

East Quantoxhead – see pp. 7–9.

Enmore (GR ST239352)

Renowned for its village school built by the rector, Revd John Poole, cousin of the benefactor Tom Poole of Nether Stowey. Open in 1810 it was the first free elementary school in England and still remains the village school today. The exterior has scarcely changed over the years. The rector also wrote a book, *The Village School Improved* which was recommended by Wordsworth. Six small cottages that still stand by the roadside were built at the same time to provide a regular rent income for the maintenance of the school. Revd John Poole was rector here for sixty years and built the rectory with a well-stocked garden. It is now called Poole House, where a later incumbent, Revd E.H. Smith, wrote his book *Quantock Life and Rambles*.

Enmore Castle. (Photograph by Chris Chapman.)

The church is a mixture of old and new with a Norman south doorway, a fine tower dating from about 1500 with unusual tall pinnacles, and the chancel and north aisle heavily restored in 1873. The well-carved dark oak pulpit is Jacobean, and two helmets by the chancel arch once belonged to the Malet family, who lived not far from the church at Enmore Castle. A board hanging close by lists twenty-two generations of the family who worshipped here from the time of the Norman Conquest in 1066 up to 1681. William Malet, called 'The Hammer', carried the standard of William the Conqueror at the Battle of Hastings, and in 1215 Sir William Malet was among the signatories of Magna Carta at Runnymede.

Enmore Castle eventually passed into the hands of John Perceval, Earl of Egmont, who around 1770 pulled down the old building and replaced it with what at the time was described as 'a singular structure, a large quadrilateral embattled pile of reddish, dark coloured stone'. On several occasions Coleridge walked from Nether Stowey to stay at the castle as friend and guest of Lord Egmont who greatly admired the poet's literary work. It was entered by a drawbridge over a dry moat 40 ft wide and 16 ft deep. This pseudo-castle was a huge affair and it is not surprising that some of it was pulled down in 1833 and converted into the more liveable building standing there today. It now overlooks the 18 hole Enmore Park golf club. The village today has no post office but there are still two inns, the Enmore Inn and the Tynte Arms Inn.

Goathurst (GR ST256344)

The name implies that this Domesday manor was once a wooded area with wild goats. The red rubble sandstone church of St Edmund was rebuilt around 1500 when the walls were no doubt rendered with white limewash. In the north chancel aisle is a fine monument to Sir Nicholas Halswell, died 1633, with recumbent figures of him, his wife, and nine children kneeling, six sons along one side, and three daughters at the end. Also in the aisle is a cabinet with a clarinet bought in 1827 for the church musicians who accompanied the singing of the psalms and anthem. In the tower arch are some unusually large hatchments and interesting charity bequest boards. Eight early bequests were amalgamated in 1974 under the 'Goathurst in Need Charity' and include the almshouses near the church built by Sir Charles Kemeys Tynte in 1780, and various gifts amounting to £1,200. On the north wall of the nave is a marble monument to Sir Charles, died 1785, who sat as knight of the county in seven successive Parliaments. Opposite the turning to the church is the driveway to Halswell House, once through 230 acres of wooded parkland with a large herd of fallow deer and a heronry, but today through open farmland. The three-storeyed house of seven bays was built in 1689 by Sir Halswell Tynte who also erected in the grounds various classical structures which included a Doric rotunda, a temple with Ionic columns, and a stepped pyramid. During the Second World War the house was taken over by the military with a prisoner-of-war camp for 700 Italian soldiers housed in wooden huts in the park. Many of the prisoners worked on local farms, and eventually some lived-in with farmers and their families. After the war the house was unoccupied and neglected, but is now slowly being restored.

Holford (GR ST157411)

A turning off the A39 by the Plough Inn leads to the church and village of Holford set at the junction of Hodder's Combe and Holford Combe. Writing in 1891 the Revd W. Nichols refers to 'Hodder's Combe or Adder's Combe', and suggests the name

Holford is derived from 'hill ford'. In Domesday Book it is written 'Holeford', so perhaps the name means 'ford in the hollow' which certainly fits the situation well.

In 1797 William Wordsworth and his sister Dorothy came to live at Alfoxton House (they always called it Alfoxden) a mile from the little church at Holford. The village frequently lay on their route when visiting Coleridge and Tom Poole at Nether Stowey, 3 miles away. They were especially enchanted by water rushing down Holford Glen with its rocky water slides overhung by ferns and shaded by huge oaks, ash and beeches. The largest cascade by the footbridge is called 'The Poet's Waterfall' with the scenery little changed from the days when Dorothy Wordsworth delighted to bring their literary visitors to see the stream from the hills tumbling over rocks in the deep gorge on its way to Kilve and the sea.

The church is picturesque but of little interest, its low tower with a saddleback roof is the oldest part, the rest a nineteenth-century rebuilding. At one time there was a project to enlarge the tower as a memorial to Wordsworth but nothing came of it apart from a drawing in the *Builder* of 1891. The 1904 Ordnance Survey map marks a disused silk mill in The Glen which seems to have flourished until about 1800. Close by is the village green, sometimes called 'the Bowling Green' with space for parking cars and the start of several walks into the hills. This can also be a good starting point for taking the public footpath that goes through Alfoxton Park. By the park entrance is the old Dog Pound and site of the cottage where Christopher Trickey lived. He was an old huntsman known to Wordsworth and was the subject of his poem 'Simon Lee'.

It is a delightful walk up Holford Combe in the springtime with the banks of the stream and the hedgerows full of wild flowers and the robin, blackcap, thrush and blackbird singing joyfully. This part of the combe is sometimes called 'Butterfly Combe' and in the old days it was known as 'Tannery Combe' for half a mile up is Combe House Hotel, a seventeenth-century house once part of a busy tannery. Its giant 27 foot diameter water-wheel still projects through the roof of an outbuilding. The tanyard closed in 1900 but the wheel was put to use for another fifty years to provide electricity for the hotel and power for stone breaking, a sawbench, a chaff-cutter and even a shoe-polishing machine.

Opposite: Halswell House, Goathurst. (Photograph by Chris Chapman.)

Kilve and Lilstock – see pp. 9–11.

Mr Trebble, the Old Tannery Water-wheel, Holford. (Photograph by Chris Chapman.)

Nether Stowey (GR ST190397)

This most interesting village lies under the east Quantock foothills, the Saxon name indicating a 'stone way' for it linked the royal manors of Cannington and Williton. Nether Stowey is the largest of the Quantock villages with a fine mixture of ancient and nineteenth-century buildings. There are three main streets: Castle Street, accompanied by a stream, running down from the castle mount to join Lime Street at The Cross and continuing on as St Mary's Street to Court House and the parish church. There is a small car park at the library near the top of

Castle Street. The library and an information centre is housed in the old village school built in 1813 by the self-taught tanner, Tom Poole, friend of Coleridge and Wordsworth. His cousin Charlotte Poole, writing on 22 March 1813 says, 'Stowey school opens next Monday in a very good room built by Mr. Tom Poole.' On 1 April 1813 she notes there are 85 children, but by 27 April numbers had increased to 118. At first Tom Poole lived in a Georgian house lower down in Castle Street now named Poole House, and after 1802 in St Mary's Street in another Georgian house called The Old House.

Stowey Castle was an eleventh-century motte and bailey with a commanding view over the village, and was probably demolished when Lord Audley built Stowey Court next to the church in the fifteenth century. Lord Audley was implicated in a rebellion against Henry VII and was executed in 1497. A handsome eighteenth-century gazebo stands on the outer wall of Stowey Court where the ladies of the day had a fine view of the comings and goings of Nether Stowey folk. Except for the tower, the church of St Mary was entirely rebuilt in 1850. Tom Poole's grave is near the west door, and inside is a marble memorial plaque to this remarkable man. At the top of Lime Street is the cottage, now owned by the National Trust, where the poet Coleridge lived and wrote his finest verse from 1796 to 1800. The story of Coleridge and his patron Tom Poole is told in Chapter Five. Nether Stowey has a wide range of shops and there is a most useful booklet *Nether Stowey, A Village Trail* obtainable from the library and from the bookshop in Castle Street.

Over Stowey (GR ST185385)

This is a large parish with a scattered population of about 400, on the east side of the Quantocks. As the name implies it is the 'higher stone way' with Nether Stowey the 'lower stone way'. There is no village centre, just a few houses near the church, and four small hamlets of Adscombe, Aley, Marsh Mills and Plainsfield. Spring is the best time to visit Over Stowey when the churchyard is full of primroses and daffodils. The church, dedicated to St Peter and St Paul, has a late fifteenth-century tower and a chancel and nave enlarged during the Victorian period when two stained glass windows by Burne-Jones were added. A wall monument to two local farmers, James and John Rich of nearby Cross Farm, includes a plough, harrow, rakes and a beehive. They also gave the large brass chandelier, and left £100 to support the Sunday school, which in 1826 had 25 boys and 25 girls attending the Sunday morning class.

Gazebo, Stowey Court, Nethe Stowey. (Photograph by Lesle Thomas.)

The £100 was left in the hand of Thomas Poole who paid interest at 4½ per cent.

Henry Labouchere, Liberal MP and member of various Liberal governments between 1832 and 1858, built and lived at Quantock Lodge in the parish. He was created Lord Taunton in 1859 and died in 1869 and is buried in the churchyard here. The Revd William Holland, rector of Over Stowey from 1789 to 1819 gives a fascinating account of life in the parish in his diary first published in 1984. He was a high Tory and a rigid Churchman with fierce strictures on all who crossed his path. Of his own brother Jeffrey, also a clergyman, he wrote on 7 December 1801, 'A man of no principle, unfortunate in his marriage, dissolute and even desperate in his manners.'

Spaxton (GR ST225371)

The church of St Margaret with its great lime trees, the fifteenth-century Court Farm, the old mill and millpond with moorhen and grey wagtail, make a delightful group to the north of this straggling village. Also in this group are six almshouses built under the will of Revd Joseph Cooke, dated 17 July 1708, and according to a tablet, 'Improved and Restored in 1958'. Under the will one of the rooms was to be allotted to 'a civil, honest poor man of the parish of Spaxton to read prayers twice a day to the said poor people, and to pay such reader 4 shillings a week'. The trustees were also required to pay Elizabeth Freeman 2s 6d per week for teaching fifteen poor children of the parish. Now Spaxton has a primary school built by Lord Taunton in 1860, and a Methodist church opened in 1855.

Bench ends in the parish church bear the dates 1536 and 1561 and another shows a fuller working on a length of cloth with the tools of his trade spread around him. This was a time when spinning and weaving wool was an important cottage industry in many Quantock villages. Parts of the church go back to the thirteenth century but it was substantially rebuilt in the fifteenth-century Perpendicular style. It is a most attractive and light building and between the vestry and chancel are the figures of a knight in armour and his wife. They probably represent Sir John Hill, died 1434, and his wife Cecily. His will requested burial in Spaxton chancel and he left money for the rebuilding of the tower. The south chapel now holds the altar and reredos from St Mary's church, Charlynch which was closed in 1988 for conversion to a house.

The combined post office and shop is at Four Forks at the east end of the village. Here a garage has replaced the workshops of the blacksmith, wheelwright and carpenter, and just round the corner is the old bakehouse and the Lamb Inn. In between is a derelict chapel, enclosure walls, and buildings of the Agapemonite or Abode of Love religious colony. This was founded in 1841 by the 29-year-old Revd Henry Prince, one time curate at nearby Charlynch. Peak numbers were around 100 but dropped to 50 in 1926, and to just a handful when it closed in 1958. Members were largely women but with a few married couples. There was constant outside talk both locally and in the press about just what was going on within its high walls, but its final years were seemly enough, though with unorthodox beliefs and practices.

West Bagborough (GR ST168337)

There is an East Bagborough in the parish but the name has disappeared from recent Ordnance Survey maps with Terhill taking its place. The village of West Bagborough with its Rising Sun Inn, called the Shepherd's Crook up to the First World War, and pottery and shop, shelters below Bagborough Hill. The church of St Pancras, set in the spacious parkland of Bagborough House, climbs a little higher up the hillside. The slate-roofed house is Georgian with white walls and fronted by an attractive Ionic colonnade of five bays. For the past 250 years it has been the home of the Popham family. William Wordsworth and his wife, Mary, stayed at the house for a few days in 1841 during their nostalgic farewell tour of the West Country. Fenwick Bisset, renowned among masters of staghounds, married the heiress of Bagborough, and in 1860 set about re-establishing a herd of red deer on the Quantocks. This was done by removing young deer from Exmoor; some of these soon made their way back to their previous haunts, but sufficient remained for the herd to be established on the Quantock hills.

The path up to the church is part of the old way to Triscombe, and the abandoned sweeping carriage drive to the house from the west can be traced in the sloping grassland. The fifteenth-century church was restored in 1874 when a new porch was added complete with a sundial dated 1648. Some good quality additions were made in the 1920s including the rood, font cover and stained glass. Triscombe is a hamlet on the edge of Bagborough parish. Here the thatched Blue Ball Inn nestles below Wills Neck and close to a vast working quarry.

The road of Bagborough and up on to the hills passes by Tilbury Farm and through an avenue of beeches to a car park on Lydeard Hill, a starting place for a number of fine walks. Tilbury Park below the farm is watched over by a strange statue looking like some classical hunter with flowing locks, a dog crouching at heel, and set on a canopied stone seat. John Page writing in 1890 says the statue is an 'unexpressively hideous and inartistic nude figure, presumably a man, and with less doubt a hunter. The generally barbarous appearance would fix as the date of its erection the debased period of a hundred years ago.' Time has mellowed the features just a little, and in the spring of 1994 the statue collapsed, but plans are in hand to set it up once more.

West Quantoxhead (GR ST110417)

Revd John Collinson in 1791 names it 'St. Audries or West Quantockshead', and it is still frequently called St Audries by local folk. This name comes from the church dedicated to St Etheldreda or St Audrey. She is best known as the founder and abbess of a monastery built at Ely in AD 672 on the site where the present cathedral stands. Old maps show that the village of West Quantoxhead was grouped around the church, but early in the nineteenth century it was cleared and rebuilt half a mile away on a

Triscombe stone quarry.
(Photograph by Chris
Chapman.)

spur of the Quantocks with extensive views towards the sea and
Exmoor. In 1854 the old church was also demolished and two years
later the one we see today was opened. It is built of Doulting stone
taken from Shepton Mallet, the nave piers are of Babbacombe
marble, and the roof is Somerset oak. The Norman font is the only
old feature in the church.

Below the church is the old manor-house, once the home of Lord
St Audries, which was largely rebuilt when the village was moved.
Then the house had fine lawns and the wooded deer park was
stocked with both red and fallow deer. In 1939 the house became a
public school for girls but this has now closed. Staple Farm, near the
centre of the village, was probably built 300 years ago, and opposite
the farm a narrow road changing to a rough track, climbs up to
Staple Plain and to a parking area overlooking Weacombe Combe.
Hidden away below is the hamlet and the ancient farmhouse of
Weacombe.

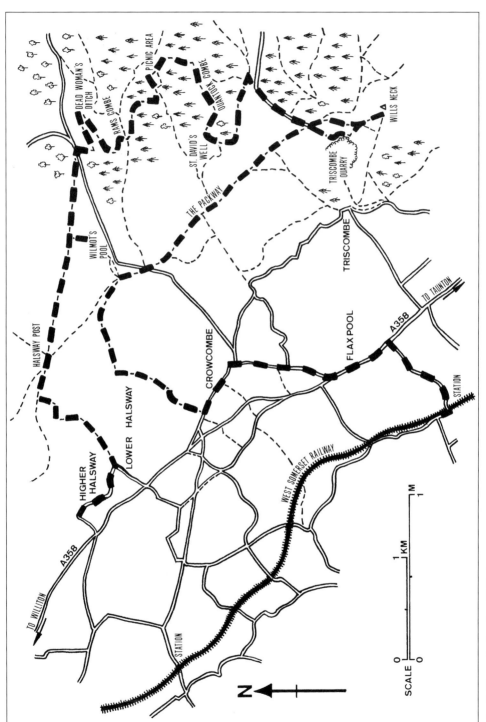

Map 5. (Drawn by Jonathan White.)

Crowcombe to Halsway Manor

This is a combined moorland and woodland walk from Crowcombe via Crowcombe Combe Gate, Great Hill, Marrow Hill, Triscombe Quarry, Wills Neck, Triscombe Stone, Hart Hill, St David's Well, Lords Ball, Rams Combe, Dead Woman's Ditch, Wilmot's Pool and Halsway Post to Halsway Manor. Distance: about 10 miles. Map: ST 03/13.

> The walk as described below starts in the village of Crowcombe (GR ST140367) where there is a car park behind Church House. It is, however, possible to come by the West Somerset Railway to Crowcombe station and walk up into the village along the road for 1½ miles.

Crowcombe. We first hear of Crowcombe in Saxon times as the manor owned by the Church at Winchester, in the Kingdom of Wessex. After the Norman Conquest it was given to William's brother, Robert of Mortain, and under him the manor was held by a family who assumed the manor's name 'de Crowcombe'.

The twelfth and thirteenth centuries saw a great period of colonization and new farms were created by the free peasants, armed with charters from the lords of the manor, who granted them land on payment of annual rents. The later creation of a borough by the lord of the manor was also speculation on his part, as he hoped to see his village grow through the granting of a market and its subsequent attendance, filling the coffers with rents and tolls which would supplement a modest income from agriculture.

Although then on the main route from Taunton to the port of Watchet and entered by traffic across the Quantocks, Crowcombe never grew on a grand scale, but the thirteenth-century market cross bears witness to those times.

On your right stands the Church of the Holy Ghost. This is an exceptionally beautiful church with a very fine late Perpendicular south porch and aisle. The church tower, as well as housing the bells, was a way of displaying the wealth of the parish to its neighbours. This tower once had a very fine spire but it came crashing down in a thunderstorm in 1725. If you look carefully at the east end of the churchyard you will find the pinnacle masquerading as a gravestone.

Somerset is rich in the bench carver's art and Crowcombe is no exception. Many of the bench ends depict the vine, a symbol of fruitfulness, and also the green man with grape stems coming out of his mouth, representing a god of fertility.

One bench end portrays two men spearing a two-headed dragon. Below this carving, one dragon head is swallowing the vine and another appears to be swallowing a deer or lamb. There is also an amusing carving of a bat. The great 'Vurm', a serpent-like dragon who fed on human flesh and devoured cattle and sheep, is an old Quantock legend. This panel could well be relating to this story. The dragon eats the vine and the animal and so must be killed by man. Perhaps the bat is thrown in for good measure as proof that these horrors exist!

The wrought iron chandelier – a superb example of the blacksmith's art – was designed by local craftsman, James Horrobin of Minehead. It was given by the Revd Peter Birkett, a former rector, as a memorial to his wife.

On the north of the church is the old chapel, remade in 1665, by Thomas Carew for the family of Crowcombe Court. There are seven diamond-shaped hatchments in the chapel, an unusual collection. The word hatchment comes from 'achievement' and when someone of note died in the parish (for instance the lord of the manor) it was customary to hang his coat of arms on the gatehouse or entrance porch of his residence as a mark of respect.

Bench end in Crowcombe Church. (Photograph by Chris Chapman.)

Leaving the church you will see the fifteenth-century church house on the opposite side of the road.

Church houses date back to the middle of the fifteenth-century. They were built, often by the parishioners themselves, when the church authorities decided to remove all commercial and recreational activities from the church. They were used for general parish purposes including church ales and later, in the eighteenth century, this one at Crowcombe housed six poor of the parish on the ground floor while serving as a schoolroom above.

Church houses were originally single storey with open timbered roofs, usually of oak finished with thatch. Although no longer thatched this is a graceful example, having cambered collars and curved wind-bracing between the trusses. There is a village pound for stray animals attached to the building's western end.

Walk up the village street.

On your right is the market cross – it was the centre of the old village market dating from 1226 and its steps show signs of wear from those who sat on them selling their produce.

On your right, just past the post office, are some small steps leading to a path through the fields up to Crowcombe Park Gate. This is a steep climb. As you reach the top Hurley Beacon will be on your left. Follow the path past the lodge to Crowcombe Combe Gate. From here walk in a south-easterly direction over Great Hill and Marrow Hill to Triscombe Quarry.

Triscombe Quarry. As you first approach the quarry you can hear little of the activity going on below. Fortunately your way is then blocked by a strong fence and a sign saying 'Danger – Deep Quarry'. It is fascinating to see the workings and the dumper trucks look like tiny Dinky toys. There are also magnificent views to Exmoor from here.

Many smaller quarries have been worked on the Quantocks in the past and beautiful buildings like Crowcombe Church and the church house are built of quarried stone.

For some, a working landscape is a welcome sight, and the resources of Triscombe Quarry have a ready market as roadstone and building aggregates. One wonders, though, how long this can continue. Millions of tons have already been taken from here and activity on this scale is certain to have a detrimental effect on the area.

Walk up to Wills Neck – 'the ridge of the Wealas'.

At 1,260 ft, Wills Neck is the highest point on the Quantocks. In the seventh century the invading Saxons dubbed the ancient tribes of

WALK 4

The Bronze Age Triscombe Stone. (Photograph by Chris Chapman.)

Britain as the 'Wealas' (Welsh) and here in the Quantocks they were met with considerable resistance. These hilltops were the last Celtic strongholds in this part of Somerset before the Celts were driven out and subdued. Later in history the hill was used as a beacon with a fire signal-pit that visually links with Dunkery Beacon on Exmoor. As you turn around to head back to Triscombe Stone there are magnificent views to Bridgwater, Glastonbury Tor, the Bristol Channel and west to Exmoor.

Walk back to Triscombe Stone.

This small worn standing stone of great antiquity now looks a little lost and out of place in its car park setting! It is reputed to have mysterious powers and will grant a wish to those who sit on it.

> Take the road in a north-easterly direction and after half a mile, turn left on to the forest track and walk to St David's Well, via Hart Hill, at the head of Quantock Combe.

Downstream at Adscombe is the ruin of a tenth-century chapel which belonged to Athelney Abbey, and St David's Well may be contemporary with this. Holy wells are often earlier pagan sites, their magic–religious significance transferred from goddesses and water spirits to saints and early missionaries. Prehistoric man erected standing stones by springs, acknowledging water as the giver of life and treating it as divine and sacred. It must have been a great mystery to see water bubbling from the earth at the birth of some stream or river.

> Walk up through the thinned plantation of Douglas fir to Lord's Ball and down the forest track to Rams Combe.

The Forestry Commission has discreetly signposted plantations of different trees. Note the European larch, which has not been successful due to its susceptibility to fungi and beetle. In the bottom of the combe are Western hemlock which are very graceful and grow to a height of over 100 ft. There is a camping and picnic area in Rams Combe.

> Follow the footpath in a northerly direction until you meet another forest trail near the top of the hill. Turn east and when you reach a gate take the track west until you reach Dead Woman's Ditch.

The origin and purpose of Dead Woman's Ditch is difficult to quantify, but it is believed to be Saxon. It would seem to have some connection with Dowsborough hill-fort to the north, which is known to be Iron Age. It could have been built as a type of barrier or defence across the ridge and certainly ancient trackways met and crossed here, including the Saxon harepath which ran from Combwich on the River Parrett to the port of Barnstaple.

Locally the name is attributed to the place where, in the eighteenth century, John Walford threw his wife's body after murdering her in a fitful rage. This is thought to be untrue however as the name appears long before this event (which didn't happen at this spot and its significance has been lost or confused).

Cross the road and walk in a westerly direction to Wilmot's (or Withyman's) Pool.

Wilmot's Pool is a dew-pond. This is man-made and was dug as a watering hole for cattle and sheep – there being few natural springs with a large supply of water on the top of the hills. The pond appears on an old map held by the Somerset Record Office. Note the tumulus on its southern edge.

Dew-ponds occur in many other places in Britain and are known by other names such as cloud, mist and fog ponds. There is considerable argument as to how and why they work and it may well be a combination of different theories.

They are usually about 40 ft across and like this one have a gentle profile so that the animals can easily reach the water's edge. Usually only a few feet deep, they were often made by lining the dug depression with straw, covered with stone rubble, and then sealed with a lining of puddled clay. The straw was supposed to insulate the pond from the warmth of the earth, so that at night the water would cool. This in turn would encourage dew to form over the pond's surface and so replenish the supply. Rain, however, must also play a role, and we've all experienced the droplets of water that cling to hair and clothing as we walk the tops in a mist. It seems likely therefore that cloud, mist and rain all play their part in the filling of the pond.

Continue in a westerly direction to Halsway Post and then drop down into the combe, past the disused quarries, and finish at Halsway Manor.

Halsway was at one time the hunting lodge of Cardinal Beaufort who saw Joan of Arc tried at Rouen, but the present impressive building is a folk centre.

You may return along the road to Crowcombe or, if you came by train, you can continue on down the lane below Halsway Manor for about a mile to Stogumber station.

CHAPTER FIVE

Quantock Writers and Poets

T he Quantocks have seen a number of writers: Walter Raymond who lived at Nether Stowey, Sir Henry Newbolt at Aisholt, and Phyllis Bottome at Over Stowey. Supreme among this select band were Samuel Taylor Coleridge and William Wordsworth, who for one brief year discussed, planned, and brought to birth the romantic school of English poetry typified in the title and contents of the book they wrote together, *Lyrical Ballads*.

Walter Raymond, 1852–1931, retired from business as a glove manufacturer in Yeovil when he was forty, and wrote fifteen full-length books, chiefly novels and stories about the crafts and customs of the West Country. In 1908 he moved into a cottage in Withypool in the heart of Exmoor, paying a weekly rent of 1*s*. He described the cottage and some of the characters he met there in his book, *A Book of Simple Delights*, in 1909. In 1918 he moved to Nether Stowey, living in a house close to Stowey Court. Here he wrote his novel, *Verity Thurston*, a long tale of smuggling around Somerset, and a book of essays, *Under the Spreading Chestnut Tree*, printed by the Somerset Folk Press. By 1925 he was seventy-three and he moved to a modern cottage in Street to be near to friends. He died in 1931.

Sir Henry Newbolt, 1862–1938, poet and naval historian, spent much time in the little village of Aisholt writing, as he said, 'under the thatch in that beloved valley,' for he lived in the old thatched schoolhouse. He wrote of Aisholt church, 'It has that unmistakable mark of the centuries, so quiet and eternal, so far from the shop-made or the shoddy, and it stands so perfectly with the woods close behind and the village winding down the hill past it.' Two of his poems are in the *Oxford Book of English Verse*, but not his 'Drake's Drum' and 'Admirals All' for which he is perhaps best known. In 1923 he was appointed the official historian of the British Navy and completed volumes four and five of the *Naval History of the Great War, 1914–18*. He was knighted in 1915, and made a Companion of Honour in 1922.

As a child, the novelist Phyllis Bottome lived in the rectory at Over Stowey where her father was the rector from 1887 to 1892. In her biography *Search for a Soul* she tells of her early years in this tiny Quantock village where the country women curtsied to the lord of the manor and his lady, and the menfolk doffed their caps. Now, the lord and lady have gone, the big house is a school, and the whole social structure of village life has changed. Phyllis Bottome could write 'Over Stowey was the real home of my heart. The beauty of the waterfalls and streams, the deep red earth, the strong wiry bracken, the lovely heather hills, the fragrant drenched woods, full of moss and ferns; these were the master-pieces of my childhood's work.' These natural things remain, and remain largely unchanged for us to revel in today.

Coleridge was a son of the vicar of Ottery St Mary, Devon, a somewhat eccentric parson who would give out his text in Hebrew or Latin to the astonishment and admiration of his rural congregation. Part way through his studies at Cambridge Samuel Coleridge suddenly left to enlist with the 15th Dragoons, but after a few months the purchase of his release was arranged and he returned to Cambridge. Here he met up with Robert Southey, afterwards the Poet Laureate, and the two developed a scheme to set up a commune on the Susquehanna River in North America. Towards this end Coleridge married Sara Fricker in 1795, and Southey her sister Edith. Perhaps their wives knocked some sense into them for their plans to emigrate were soon dropped.

From 1793 to 1796 Coleridge contributed verses to the *Morning Chronicle* and also started a journal, *The Watchman,* which only had a brief life of ten numbers. These early literary efforts brought him into contact with Joseph Cottle, bookseller and publisher of Bristol who printed *Lyrical Ballads*. It was in Bristol in the autumn of 1795 that Coleridge seems to have met up with William Wordsworth and his sister Dorothy for the first time. They were there to arrange with John Pinney about the renting of his house at Racedown, Dorset, and Coleridge was on a lecture tour of the city. Also around this time Coleridge made contact with Thomas Poole of Nether Stowey, a tanner of some means, and a man of liberal views and a lover of books. So in the space of about a year there was a meeting of two budding writers, a publisher, and an unlikely benefactor.

Coleridge was attracted to Tom Poole and his well-stocked bookroom, and after some correspondence Tom Poole was able to get a cottage for him in Lime Street, Nether Stowey. Coleridge, with his wife, Sara, and baby son, David Hartley, moved in on 31

December 1796 and for a while they had a lodger, Charles Lloyd, son of a banker, who had aspirations to write poetry and whose board money helped towards the household expenses. The Lime Street cottage consisted of two small rooms, one on either side of a front door, a narrow corridor leading to a kitchen, and three bedrooms beneath a thatched roof. A door at the rear gave access to a long garden with a lane at the bottom leading to Tom Poole's garden and house. A well in the garden and a stream flowing by their front door gave them all the water needed.

Of their first weeks in the cottage Coleridge said, 'We are very happy, and my little David Hartley grows a sweet boy. I raise potatoes, and all manner of vegetables: have an orchard, and shall raise corn (with a spade) enough for my family. We have two pigs and ducks and geese. We have whatever milk we want from T. Poole.' In a further letter he describes his day's routine:

> From seven till half-past eight I work in my garden. From breakfast till twelve I read and compose, then read again, feed the pigs, poultry etc, till two o'clock; after dinner work again till tea; from tea till supper, review. So jogs the day, and I am happy. I have society, my friend T. Poole and as many acquaintances as I can dispense with. There are a number of very pretty young women in Stowey, all musical, and I am an immense favourite, for I pun, conundrumwise, listen and dance. The last is a recent acquirement.

Coleridge's horticultural pursuits seem to have been short-lived; it is doubtful if he ever paid the small rent of the cottage, and by the middle of 1797 Tom Poole was already seeking subscriptions from his literary friends towards supporting the occupants of the Lime Street cottage. With the arrival of William Wordsworth and Dorothy at Alfoxton (they always spelt it Alfoxden) there was different spadework to be done; the exchange of almost daily visits, lengthy discussions on the nature of poetry and writing, reading of each other's verse, planning for its publication, and long walks through the wooded Quantock combes, up to the heathy hilltops, down to the stony beach at Kilve. During his few years under the Quantock hills Coleridge did his best work, 'Kubla Khan', 'Frost at Midnight', the greater part of 'Christabel', and 'This Lime-Tree Bower, My Prison'. These were joyful, hopeful days and he could write:

> And now, beloved Stowey! I behold
> Thy church-tower, and methinks the four huge elms
> Clustering, which mark the mansion of my friend;
> And close behind them, hidden from my view,
> Is my own lowly cottage, where my babe
> And by babe's mother dwell in peace!

The fifteenth-century church tower remains much as Coleridge must have seen it, but the body of the church was rebuilt in the nineteenth century. In his time there was a minstrel gallery for the band which accompanied the singing of the psalms and anthem, and in 1797 a bassoon was added perhaps suggesting the lines in 'The Rime of the Ancient Mariner':

The wedding guest here beat his breast,
For he heard the loud bassoon.

'My friend' of the poem was, of course, Tom Poole; generous,
thoughtful, patient, and ever on hand to encourage and help. He was
a bachelor aged thirty-two, and lived in a Georgian house in Castle
Street, Nether Stowey, now called Poole House, and from 1802 in
The Old House, St Mary's Street. His great pride was his bookroom,
well stocked and regularly furnished with new volumes. This was a
great attraction to Coleridge for he could slip across his garden and
into Poole's property and up to the bookroom for quiet seclusion and
study. After Coleridge had left for the Lake District, Poole wrote and
tried to induce him to return at least for a winter, 'Come and pass it
here, I have made a nice, very nice, bookroom in which you may
regulate the climate as you like, in which there is even a bed though
you can't see it. I promise to get any books you want.'

Tom Poole was not only a loyal friend to both Coleridge and
Wordsworth, he was also a most practical benefactor to his native
village. He started benefit societies for men and women, to help in
sickness and old age: the Quantock Savings Bank, the building with
the name stands in Lime Street; and he built the village school in
1813. This was the second free elementary school in England and

continued up to 1979. It is now a county branch library and a Quantock information centre, a use we are sure Tom Poole would have approved of. Besides Coleridge and William and Dorothy Wordsworth, his other guests included Charles Lamb, William Hazlitt, De Quincey and Robert Southey, who all achieved eminence in the world of literature, Josiah and Thomas Wedgwood (the potters), and Sir Humphrey Davy, inventor of the miner's safety lamp. Davy dedicated his last book to 'Thomas Poole, Esq., of Nether Stowey, in remembrance of thirty years of continued and faithful friendship.'

We get a picture of Tom Poole by De Quincey who described him as a

stout, plain looking farmer, leading a bachelor life in a rustic old fashioned house; the house, however proving to be amply furnished with modern luxuries, and especially with a good library, superbly mounted in all departments bearing on political philosophy, and the farmer turning out a polished Englishman, who had travelled extensively, and had so entirely devoted himself to the service of his humble fellow-countrymen – the hewers of woods and drawers of water in this part of Somerset – that for many miles around he was the general arbiter of their disputes, the guide and counsellor of their difficulties, besides being appointed executor and guardian to his children by every third man who died in or about the town of Nether Stowey.

With the encouragement of Coleridge and the support of Tom Poole, William and Dorothy Wordsworth secured a year's lease of Alfoxton House on the outskirts of Holford. In a letter to Robert Southey, his brother-in-law, Coleridge describes the property as, 'A gentleman's seat, with a park and woods, elegantly and completely furnished, with nine lodging rooms, three parlours, and a hall, in the most beautiful and romantic situation by the seaside, 4 miles from Stowey – this we have got for Wordsworth at the rate of twenty-three pounds a year, taxes included! The park and woods are his for all purposes he wants them, and the large gardens are altogether and entirely his.' The owner of Alfoxton was Langley St Albyn, then a boy of ten and away at school in Bristol. Wordsworth was able to take such a large place mainly because he had just received a legacy of £900 left him by a friend, Raisley Calvert. Early in July of 1797 Coleridge borrowed Tom Poole's chaise and drove William and Dorothy the 40 miles from Dorset to Nether Stowey where they

Alfoxton House, home of
Wordsworth. (Drawing by
Jonathan White.)

spent a few days in the Lime Street cottage before moving into Alfoxton. Charles Lamb was staying with the Coleridges at the time so it must have been quite a crush for them all.

Immediately they began to explore the countryside around, enchanted by the rolling Quantock hills, the wooded combes, the lively streams dashing over mossy rocks and flowing noisily down from springs high up on the open moor. Reaching the top they gazed breathless across vast landscapes of hills, valleys and sea. On the second day . . . but let Coleridge tell the story: 'Charles Lamb has been with me for a week. He left me Friday morning. The second day after Wordsworth came to me, dear Sara emptied a skillet of boiling milk on my foot which confined me during the whole of C. Lamb's stay, and still prevents me from all walks longer than a furlong. While Wordsworth, his sister Dorothy and Charles Lamb were out one evening, sitting in the arbour of T. Poole's garden which communicates with mine, I wrote these lines.' Then Coleridge quotes a new poem he had just finished called 'This Lime-Tree Bower, My prison', where in imagination he follows the progress of his three friends through the combe and by the waterfall until:

> Now, my friends emerge
> Beneath the wide, wide heaven – and view again
> The many steepled tract magnificent
> Of hilly fields, and meadows and the sea.

91

Wordsworth was born in 1770 and was twenty-six when he and his sister Dorothy, a year younger, settled at Alfoxton. Coleridge was twenty-four and in May of 1798 wrote, 'I have now known Wordsworth for a year and some months, and my admirations – I might say my love – for his intellectual powers has increased even to this hour; and what is more important, he is a tried good man.' Coleridge was without doubt attracted to Dorothy and she to him, but he was already married, and she deeply involved in the welfare of her brother and his writing. In their first days together Coleridge wrote, 'Wordsworth and his exquisite sister are with me. She is a woman indeed! – in mind, I mean, and heart: for her person is such that, if you expected to see a pretty woman, you would think her ordinary: if you expected to see an ordinary woman, you would think her pretty! but her manners are simple, ardent, impressive, her eye watchful in minutest observation of Nature.' This last truth is clearly revealed in the journal she kept from January 1798. On 26 January she wrote, 'Walked upon the hill-tops; followed the sheep tracks till we overlooked the larger combe. Sat in the sunshine. The distant sheep-bells, the sound of the streams, the woodman winding along the half-marked road with his laden pony; locks of wool, still spangled with dewdrops; the blue grey sea, shaded with immense masses of clouds, not streaked, the sheep glittering in the sunshine. Returned through the woods, the ground strewed with the red berries of the holly.'

In a number of his lines Wordsworth acknowledges his debt to Dorothy who opened his eyes to see the rarer beauties of the sky above and the earth below, especially in days sometimes clouded with despondency.

> She whispered still that brightness would return;
> She in the midst of all, preserved me still
> A poet, made me seek beneath that name,
> and that alone, my office upon earth.

In *The Prelude* he wrote:

> A rock with torrents roaring, with the clouds
> Familiar, and a favourite of the stars:
> But thou didst plant its crevices with flowers,
> Hang it with shrubs that twinkle in the breeze,
> And teach the little birds to build the nests
> And warble in its chambers.

Dorothy gives her early impressions of Coleridge in a letter to a friend,

> You had a great loss in not seeing Coleridge. He is a wonderful man. His conversation teems with soul, mind and spirit. At first I thought him very plain, that is for about three minutes. He is pale, thin, has a wide mouth, thick lips, not very good teeth, longish, loose-growing, half-curling, rough black hair, but if you hear him speak for five minutes, you think no more of them. His eye is large and full, and not very dark, but grey. Such an eye would receive from a heavy soul the dullest expression; but it speaks every emotion of his animated mind. It has more of a poet's eye, in a fine frenzy rolling, than I ever witnessed. He has fine dark eyebrows, and an overhanging forehead.

Dorothy must have given him more than a casual glance to write such a full description.

Occasionally, Coleridge preached in Unitarian chapels and sometimes walked the 12 miles to Taunton to help out the Revd Joshua Toulmin. For a time he seriously thought of entering the ministry as a means of supporting his family. To this end he travelled to Shrewsbury with the view to becoming the Unitarian pastor in the town. William Hazlitt tells in his long essay, 'My first acquaintance with poets' how in January 1798 he walked 10 miles to Shrewsbury to hear Coleridge preach on the text, 'And He went up into the mountain to pray, Himself, alone.' Hazlitt goes on,

> He made a poetical and pastoral excursion, and to show the fatal effects of war, drew a striking contrast between the simple shepherd boy, driving his team afield, or sitting under the hawthorn piping to his flock, and the same poor country-lad, crimped, kidnapped, brought into town, made drunk at an alehouse, turned into a wretched drummer boy, with his hair sticking on end with powder and pomatum, a long cue at his back, and tricked out in the loathsome finery of the profession of blood.

It was just at this time that the Wedgwood brothers came to the rescue with an offer to Coleridge of an allowance of £150 a year. This immediately relieved him of the anxiety of supporting his wife and children, and set him free for study, writing, and critical discussions with the Wordsworths and visiting friends. Together they explored almost every corner of the Quantocks and made long excursions along the coast as far as Lynton and the Valley of Rocks in North Devon, a return trip of nearly 80 miles.

It was on one of these long coastal walks that Wordsworth and Coleridge planned the writing of a poem to help pay the expenses of the trip. The idea developed until by the end of the tour it was decided to publish jointly a small volume of poems. This came out in 1798 with the title of *Lyrical Ballads*, printed by their friend Joseph Cottle of Bristol. Coleridge contributed only three poems but included his masterpiece, 'The Rime of the Ancient Mariner'. This, together with his 'Kubla Khan' and the first part of 'Christabel' written in the cottage at Nether Stowey, ensured for him lasting fame among English poets. Wordsworth's part was a number of shorter poems, some of which have proved great favourites through the years. Among them was 'Lines composed above Tintern Abbey', 'We are seven', and one popular with local folk, 'Simon Lee the Old Huntsman'. This last poem Wordsworth tells us was composed in Holford Glen, and the huntsman's real name was Christopher Trickey who lived in a cottage on the edge of Holford Green, close to the existing Dog Pound. He said the expression, '"I dearly love their voice" was word for word from the old huntsman's lips.'

While Wordsworth seems to smile on the old man, who after his hunting days were over made a sparse living by cutting turf on the commons, the Revd William Holland from the nearby parish of Over Stowey wrote in his diary for 10 July 1800:

I mounted my horse and rode through Stowey. Then went on to the top of Quantock, saw the turfman, he shewed me the turf cut. In the afternoon the rascal called to ask me for the money and a cup of drink. What said I, before the turf is received, that is not the proper mode of proceeding but he begged hard, said he had not eaten a bit of bread since yesterday and wanted the money to procure some. I gave it like a fool as I was, but the moment he turned his back all cried out that I should never get the turf now, so that I am laughed at by everyone. His name too is Trickey, as rascally faced fellow as ever I met with.

The critics of the day were fiercely hostile to *Lyrical Ballads* which turned away from the formal and artificial style of the day to simple tales told in simple lines. As so often happens the critics have long been forgotten and *Lyrical Ballads* is still hailed as a landmark in English romantic poetry born in the Quantock country.

During his year at Alfoxton Wordsworth completed some twenty poems, many of them in scenes and places not greatly changed today. He tells how 'We are Seven' was composed while walking in the woods at Alfoxton, 'Lines Written in Early Spring' by the stream in the glen at Holford, and 'A Chosen Resort of Mine' and 'A Night Piece' on the road between Nether Stowey and Holford. 'The Thorn' was planned on 'a ridge of Quantock Hill on a stormy day on seeing the thorn', and the meeting related in 'The Last of the Flock' happened in Holford village. 'A Whirl Blast from behind the Hill' was, he says, 'observed in the holly-grove at Alfoxden'. The writing of these poems and others by Coleridge is recalled by Wordsworth in his long autobiographical poem, *The Prelude*:

> That summer, under those indulgent skies,
> Upon smooth Quantock's airy ridge we roved
> Unchecked, or loitered 'mid her sylvan combes,
> Thou in bewitching words, with happy heart,
> Didst chaunt the vision of that Ancient Man,
> The bright-eyed Mariner, and rueful woes
> Didst utter of the Lady Christabel;
> And I, associate with such labour, steeped
> In soft forgetfulness the livelong hours,
> Murmuring of him who, joyous hap, was found,
> After the perils of his moonlight ride,
> Near the loud waterfall; or her who sat
> In misery near the miserable Thorn:
> When thou dost to that summer turn thy thoughts,
> And hast before thee all which then we were,
> To thee, in memory of that happiness,
> It will be known, by thee at least, my Friend!
> Felt, that the history of a poet's mind
> Is labour not unworthy of regard.

To the rural community around Nether Stowey and Holford, Coleridge and Wordsworth together with some of their visiting friends gave grounds for much gossip and suspicion. The days were full of rumour and alarms with the French Revolution in full swing and Napoleon and his armies were advancing in Europe and threatening England. The young poets made a habit of walking abroad at all hours of the day and night, they frequently visited Kilve beach to sit on the rocks and gaze across the sea, and they appeared to have no proper occupation; all this and much more caused their neighbours to wonder if they had spies in their midst. Dorothy

Wordsworth was also a mystery to everyone. Here she was living in a mansion, surrounded by a park and deer, yet hanging out her own washing, collecting sticks in the woods, and with no servants to do the cleaning. Furthermore, she arrived with a child who no one could account for, though the truth was simple enough. The child was Basil Montagu, son of a lawyer friend, who paid the Wordsworths £50 a year towards his upkeep.

A clue to the local opinion of them all, even after the Wordsworths had left Alfoxton, can be found in the diary of Revd William Holland of the nearby parish of Over Stowey. The entry for 23 October 1799 reads, 'Went with my wife to Stowey. Saw that Democratic hoyden Mrs. Coleridge who looked like a friskey girl or something worse that I was not surprised that a Democratic Libertine should choose her for a wife. The husband gone to London suddenly, no one here can tell why. Met the patron of democrats, Mr. Thos. Poole who smiled and chatted a little. He was on his gray mare, Satan himself cannot be more false and hypocritical.'

In a roundabout way tales of them reached the Duke of Portland, then Home Secretary, and so a government agent, James Walsh, was sent down to investigate. He arrived in Nether Stowey staying at the Globe Inn on 15 August 1797 and quickly collected a variety of stories about 'Those rascalls at Alfoxden', including a recent visit by John Thelwall, a notorious Republican and French sympathizer. Walsh stayed three weeks closely following Coleridge and Wordsworth, even overhearing some conversation, and reported that they were neither French nor dangerous even if a little unsettling to the local villagers. Coleridge tells the story in chapter ten of his *Biographia Literaria* treating it in a humorous fashion. At the time, however, the affair was serious, and a note of alarm was sounded about their presence in the West Country. This 'spy' incident was no doubt a major reason for the Wordsworths being refused an extension to their lease of Alfoxton.

Unable to renew the lease, and that in spite of the best efforts of Tom Poole, William and Dorothy reluctantly left Alfoxton on 26 June 1798. For a week they stayed with the Coleridges in the cottage at Nether Stowey, and then walked on to Bristol. Here they were guests of Joseph Cottle where they made arrangements for publishing *Lyrical Ballads* which came out at the end of August. From Bristol the Wordsworths crossed by ferry into Wales, and then walked the 10 miles to Tintern Abbey. For the next few days they explored the Wye Valley and then returned to Bristol where Coleridge met up with them. On the journey back Wordsworth composed 'Lines composed above Tintern Abbey', one of his finest poems. He said, 'I began it upon leaving Tintern, after crossing the Wye, and concluded it just as I was entering Bristol.' It was ready just in time to be included in *Lyrical Ballads*.

In September the Wordsworths and Samuel Coleridge sailed for Germany. Sara Coleridge, with two children, remained at Nether Stowey under the careful eye of Tom Poole. The excursion to Germany over, the Wordsworths settled in the Lake District and Coleridge and his family followed them shortly afterwards. Coleridge twice revisited the Quantocks, once in 1801 and again in 1807 staying each time with loyal Tom Poole, as he wrote to a friend, 'wandering about among my dear old walks of Quantock and Alfoxden'. By now the Lime Street cottage had other tenants, and eventually it became an inn with a swinging signboard reading, 'Coleridge Cottage Inn'. In June 1893 a few local admirers of the poet fixed on the cottage the present tablet inscribed 'Here S.T. Coleridge made his home 1797–1800'. A committee was then formed who leased the cottage for £15 a year, and in 1908 they bought the premises for £600, and the next year handed it over to the National Trust.

Forty-three years passed before William Wordsworth returned to his Quantock haunts in 1841. It was his final visit. Almost all his old friends had gone. Coleridge died aged sixty-one in 1834 and was buried in Highgate churchyard; Tom Poole died in 1837, his tombstone is by the west door of Nether Stowey church, mourned, as a tablet within the church reads, 'for integrity of life and inestimable qualities of heart. Some of his most illustrious literary contemporaries, Wordsworth, Davy, Southey, Coleridge were his guests and conferred distinction by their visits on his native place.' Dorothy Wordsworth remained behind at Rydal Mount by the Lakes, now a sad figure with a blank and disordered mind. One can picture the thoughts and images that passed before Wordsworth on this last visit. Now Poet Laureate, hailed as England's leading literary figure, and remembering the days of youthful friends and early endeavours, and recalling the long walks over the Quantock hills, along the coast high above the Severn Sea. All the actors have now departed, but the stage is not empty. Their verses remain among the best of English verse, and the swelling hills, the long wooded combes, the water tumbling down Holford Glen to the sea at Kilve, these have scarcely changed. They wrote lines we can read, they saw the Quantock countryside as we can see it also, and revelled in its beauty.

Staple Plain to Nether Stowey

This delightful walk takes you over the northern ridge of the Quantocks giving spectacular views as well as introducing you to its quiet wooded combes. The way runs via Staple Plain, the Great Road, Holford Beeches, Alfoxton Park, Holford Glen, Holford Combe, Dowsborough hill-fort, Walford's Gibbet to Nether Stowey Castle. Distance: about 7½ miles. Map: ST 04/14.

Drive to West Quantoxhead and from the centre of the village take the narrow road by Staple Farm to the car park (GR ST116411). Follow the Great Road in an easterly direction by Beacon Hill. This 'Road' is the main track running all the way to Holford.

Map 6. (Drawn by Jonathan White.)

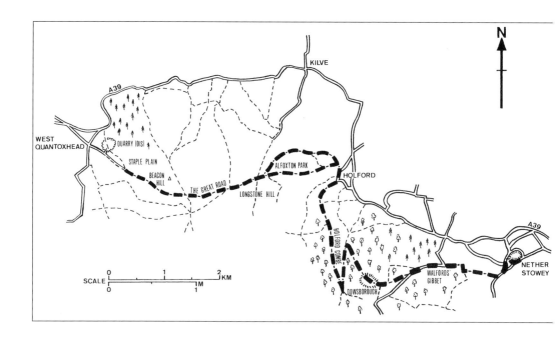

As you approached Staple Plain you will have noticed the dense colonization by wild rhododendron in Vinny Combe. In late May this valley is a blaze of colour as the vivid purple flowers mark the transition from spring to early summer. Not everyone likes this shrub. In the late seventeenth century many varieties were imported from China, India and Tibet and they became very popular in parks and gardens. However, this one, the *Rhododendron ponticum* is the only variety to grow wild on the Quantocks and thrives on acid peaty soils. It is capable of growing to a height of 20 ft or more and smothers just about any other plant in its wake. The present policy is to allow the plant its freedom in the valley but it is stopped from spreading to the open hill.

We tend to forget that these landscapes are often the process of management and another plant that is now causing concern is bracken. A member of the fern family, this primitive plant never flowers, but reproduces by spores which develop on the underside of the fully grown leaf. In open country like this its vigorous root system can spread new shoots and gain new ground each year.

So why the concern? It is thought that because of changes in grazing levels coupled with a lack of cutting (it was once used as an animal bedding material) the plant now has a hold to the detriment of most other things. In very dry summers it has been known to kill grazing cattle. The young fronds are toxic and if there is little grass around you can see how an animal would be tempted to eat its lush greenery.

There has also been some concern in recent years as the bracken is a haunt of sheep and deer ticks which have been known to infect humans with Lyme disease which can affect the heart and nervous system. Numbers of severe cases are small but it is a good idea to stick to a well-defined path when the bracken is up and tuck your trousers into your socks!

Continue along the Great Road, and under Longstone Hill which eventually drops down to Holford Beeches at the southern edge of Alfoxton Park. You may prefer to make a detour and take the track around the back of the house but we suggest staying on the Great Road and walking down to Holford (GR ST157411).

The long line of Holford Beeches are some of the oldest on the Quantocks and, as saplings, could well have been there in Wordsworth's time. One has a date of 1868 carved into its trunk though now the figures are very stretched by the increasing girth of the tree.

Holford Beeches and the Great Road. (Photograph by Chris Chapman.)

William and his sister Dorothy rented Alfoxton in 1797 and wandered these hills with their friend Samuel Coleridge who lived nearby at Nether Stowey. They were cultured people with time on their hands, writing poetry and soaking up the air. Many of their writings took inspiration from these parts, with Coleridge at his best with poems such as 'Christabel' and 'The Rime of the Ancient Mariner'.

At the end of the Great Road is a curious stone building on the left known locally as the Dog Pound. It is claimed to have housed stray dogs, but it is more likely to have been used to imprison stray sheep or cattle from the common. A theory for the odd slits in the wall is that a passer-by on horseback could survey the animals inside. The moulding depicting a dog on the south-east wall is the coat of arms of the St Albyn family of Alfoxton.

From the Dog Pound, turn left into Alfoxton Wood and then take the footpath on your right down into Holford Glen.

Holford Glen. This is a magical place and was a favourite haunt of the Wordsworths. The steep sides are wooded with ancient holly and a footbridge spans the glen. If you wish, there is a difficult scramble down to the river bank, but you do gain a better sense of the place than from the bridge over the rushing water.

> **Leave the glen and walk along the road in a southerly direction up into Holford Combe.**

In just over half a mile you pass the Combe House Hotel. Note the water-wheel that cuts through the roof. This complex of buildings was at one time a tannery and relied heavily on coppiced oak bark from the woods in the combe (see under Holford, p. 71). Further up the valley you will see the remains of a small reservoir which was used to retain water for the wheel. Once released it provided a continuous and steady flow for several hours.

In spring and on a sunny day Holford Combe dances with light and sparkles with the fresh greens of oak, whortleberry and numerous woodland flowers. Note the curious mounds of the wood ant where sticks and leaves have been gathered together to form an insulated cover for their nest.

> **The upper end of Holford Combe runs into Lady Combe. At the junction take the path to your left that runs due north for about half a mile and then turns south to climb up to Dowsborough hill-fort at 1,093 ft (GR ST160392).**

Today the prospect of a spectacular view is restricted to one small area of the fort. Scrub oak has colonized the inner area and its associated ditch. No doubt some conservationists would be appalled at the suggestion of clear felling but perhaps there is a good argument for doing so here. This hill is a pleasing spectacle covered with its blanket of trees, but Iron Age people picked the site for its dominance, its view of the surrounding countryside, and its natural display of strength to a would-be invader. We wouldn't advocate felling in the valley below but it would be great to have the view our ancestors had.

> **The path runs along the edge of the fort and winds down through the woods to meet the road which runs down to Nether Stowey. In a short distance, where the road takes a sharp left-hand turn is the site of Walford's Gibbet (GR ST174395).**

As you descend from Dowsborough towards Nether Stowey the walk is a delight – even the metalled road is charming as you plunge through a tunnel of trees. Although the map tells all, a sharp bend in the road with its ancient oak and gateway to a pasture and the Severn Sea beyond, has a strange and sad sense of place. This is the scene of Walford's Gibbet, a tragedy that had taken place only a few years before the Wordsworths had moved to Alfoxton.

John Walford was a charcoal burner from Over Stowey who fell in love with the local miller's daughter, Ann Rice. The relationship foundered and he married instead a half-witted girl from the village. Life soon became unbearable and one night, on their way to the Castle of Comfort Inn, an argument broke out. Walford dealt his wife a furious and fatal blow. The following day he confessed to her murder, pleading that he was miserable and the act had not been deliberate. Sentenced to hang on the spot where the murder took place, Walford's final wish was to speak with his former lover. They whispered for several minutes and then, in a loud firm voice as the rope was tied, he pronounced 'I am guilty of the crime I am going to die for: but I did it without foretending it, and I hope God and the world have forgiven me.'

> **From the sharp bend at Walford's Gibbet take the path through the field and walk past a small disused quarry. Turn right and follow the old green lane down into Bin Combe and take a left-hand fork at the back of the cottage. This track takes you down to the road and on to Stowey Castle mound (GR ST187396).**

Nether Stowey Castle is an almost forgotten piece of history. Typical of the motte and bailey design, it is believed to have been built in the eleventh century, and it developed on a strategic site and route across the Quantocks. The medieval settlement of Nether Stowey seems to have spread from its gates and at one time a church, dedicated to St Michael, was at its entrance. In the fourteenth century a certain Lord Audley began pinching the stone from the castle for his new manor-house at the eastern edge of the village. Although little of the old castle remains, on the new site we now have the parish church, manor and farm, turning the whole focus of the village to the east.

For a few years around 1800 Samuel Taylor Coleridge lived in Nether Stowey helped by his friend and patron, Tom Poole the tanner. The cottage in which he lived and the homes of Tom Poole still remain (see under Nether Stowey, p. 72). Below the castle mound is the public library which houses a Quantock information centre.

CHAPTER SIX

The Brendon Hills
– A Working
Landscape

The Brendon Hills are just to the west of the Quantocks separated by a narrow valley carrying the West Somerset Railway line as far as Bishop's Lydeard, and the A358 to Taunton. Many of the narrow, winding roads of the Quantocks run on into the foothills of the Brendons, and the area's economy is shared between agriculture, forestry and tourism. When the search for copper and iron ore was given up on the Quantocks in the 1820s it was taken up with better success on the Brendons. A good part of the Brendons was enclosed by 1800 and laid down to farmland grass. Only Croydon Hill, Black Hill and some steep slopes were left as rough open land. Apart from Black Hill this remaining open land was in turn seized by the newly formed Forestry Commission in 1920 and planted with conifers.

Amid the hills are the villages of Luxborough, Treborough and Withiel Florey though this is little more than a scattered hamlet. An ancient ridge road runs along the spine of the Brendons from the inn at Raleigh's Cross to the Rest and Be Thankful at Wheddon Cross. This was part of the eighth-century Saxon harepath or Army Road linking Bridgwater with Barnstaple in North Devon. Until fifty years ago it was also a busy drove road along which sheep and cattle from Exmoor and North Devon were driven to Taunton market, the drovers often spending a night at the Raleigh's Cross inn. Now fairly quiet for much of the year it does carry some holiday traffic during the summer months. The highest point is Lype Hill, 1,390 ft, and this is the highest point in Somerset apart from the Exmoor hills.

Today the Brendons have a quiet rural beauty. Green fields, beech hedges, grass verges with foxgloves and rosebay willowherb, and shady conifer plantations with picnic areas and walks. However, they had a narrow escape in the nineteenth century when determined efforts were made to locate and mine copper and iron ore. The

Mrs Morgan and her daughter, Top of Incline, Brendon Hills. (Photograph by Chris Chapman.)

earliest documentary evidence relates to 1839 when Sir Thomas Lethbridge of Bishop's Lydeard and later of Chargot, Luxborough (GR SS974380), began to investigate old sixteenth-century surface workings in the hills. This initial trial was objected to by the Earl of Egremont who claimed that his right of pasture on Withiel Common also included the mineral rights. This led to a quarrel between the two and the work ceased until 1853 when the Lethbridge trustees granted a sixty-year lease to a newly formed Brendon Hills Iron Ore Company.

Two years later 4,000 tons of ore were raised, and because of serious problems of transporting it by horse and cart to the jetty at Watchet, plans were soon made to construct a railway. Work on the line started in May 1856 and a year later the railway was opened between Watchet and Roadwater. There were the usual initial problems and delays including trouble with the first engine when the stoker failed to fill the boiler before lighting the fire. However, work was pushed ahead and by December 1857 the line reached Comberow at the foot of the hills. To reach the mines and ore 800 ft above, a giant incline was constructed ¾ mile long with a gradient of 1 in 4, which was completed in 1861. By this time production had reached over 20,000 tons a year which led to a steady build-up of the mining community on top of the Brendons.

At Gupworthy there were rows of terraced houses and other

cottages, and a Bible Christian chapel that remained in use until the 1960s. An Anglican church stood in the fields half-way between Gupworthy Mine and Lower Goosemoor and was used as a school during the week. There were buildings connected with the railway and engine houses and drying houses adjoining the various pits.

The main community, however, was assembled at Brendon Hill which was adjacent to Raleigh's Cross mine and Carnarvon New Pit with Burrow Farm nearby. Sea View House was the mine manager's home, situated at a suitable distance behind a row of stables which had a Wesleyan chapel above. Beulah Chapel (still in use, GR ST028343) stood at the road junction beside the row of terraced cottages known as Beulah Cottages. Other terraced houses were named Brick Row and Sea View Terrace. There was also another church made of green-painted corrugated iron and a temperance house which was later used as a store. A shop, Davis's Stores, stood near the water-tower at the station named Top of Incline. This was run for thirty-five years by Mr Walter Davis who died in 1926. The shop was also a great social centre for whist drives, and parties from Watchet regularly went up there. By 1871 the population was 750. An insight into our changing lifestyles is presented by the fact that such a small community, served by one general store, had five churches and chapels. The railway from Watchet to Comberow was open for passengers as well as goods traffic, and passengers could also travel up The Incline at their own risk in what must have been a very uncomfortable ten-minute journey in an open truck.

From 1874 to 1878 the line carried about 19,000 passengers and 40,000 tons of ore annually. In January 1879, however, trade slumped and the Ebbw Vale Company closed its furnaces at Sirhowy and the mines closed suddenly. By the end of the year they had reopened but in 1882 the Company decided it could import ore more cheaply from Spain and the Brendon Hill mining leases were surrendered. The railway continued to run a passenger service until the end of 1898. There was a brief revival in 1907 when the Somerset Mineral Syndicate Ltd employed about seventy-five men to work Colton and Timwood mines but they were wound up by 1910. In 1912 the line was used to demonstrate an automatic breaking system for engines and two driverless trains were set to run head on towards each other. Huge crowds gathered in order to see an almighty smash but to their great disappointment the system worked! In 1917 the Ministry of Munitions commandeered the rails and in August 1924 the land and buildings of the railway were sold off.

Today, nearly all the buildings from the former mining communities at Gupworthy and Brendon Hill are in ruins apart from Sea View House and Beulah Chapel. Time has almost obscured many of the mine workings, most shafts have been filled in and entrances to adits blocked up. There are still a few relics to be seen, although it should be remembered that most of these are on private land and should not be visited without permission. The winding house at the top of The Incline stands roofless, remains of iron window frames dangle with all panes long broken. The cable ducts can be traced and the stone supports of the bridge which carried the line over the road. The Top of Incline station house is a small cottage. In the mid-1960s walls of the stone-built general shop of John Vickery could be seen with shop door and window clearly outlined but they have since fallen down. Comberow station house is a dwelling and the platform of Luxborough Road station half-way between Top of Incline and Gupworthy is now overgrown.

One of the best preserved buildings is Burrow Farm Engine House (GR ST008345). Quite recently the National Park Authority has negotiated with the landowner for public access to this. There was a siding line running to this engine house in 1863 which was taken up in the slump and then relaid in 1880 when a new shaft, Gundrys, was sunk, together with an air shaft. The tall walls of the winding house can be visited together with the chimney, brick built in its upper section. The engine house was supplied with a rotary beam engine for pumping and winding. There was a similar building at the Kennisham Hill mine near Gupworthy. Near Burrow Farm is the Naked Boy Stone, an ancient standing stone on the line of the harepath, which later came to mark the boundary between the parishes of Old Cleeve and Brompton Regis.

The route of the line can be walked from the old station house near Watchet Harbour to Washford, but the archway where it ran under the main A39 road has been filled in. This is a pleasant, level walk alongside the West Somerset Railway which still runs steam trains and is an attraction in itself. Between Washford and Roadwater there is little evidence of the former railway except the Roadwater station building which is now a cottage. The tarred road runs more or less parallel with the line past Cleeve Abbey, Torre, Beggearn Huish (where the first sod was cut in 1856), and Clitsome to Roadwater. Beyond the village it is possible to walk the actual track past Pitt Mill and so to Comberow and the foot of The Incline. There is no right of way along The Incline but a public footpath just west of Beulah Chapel on Brendon Hill crosses The Incline 600 yd from the top and goes through woods to Leigh Falls and down to Comberow and on to Roadwater.

Burrow Farm Engine House.
(Drawing by Jonathan White.)

Spoil heap, Treborough Slate Quarry. (Photograph by Lesley Thomas.)

Treborough Slate Quarry (GR ST014368)

An earlier and longer lasting Brendon Hill enterprise was the slate quarry at Treborough, for this was working by 1426 when 2,000 slates were purchased for Dunster Castle. These slates cost 20*d* and the carriage from Treborough to Dunster was 3*s* 4*d*.

In 1734 a great storm blew the roof off Luccombe Church and the damage was repaired with Treborough slates. In 1830 it was recorded that 'the quarry is now in full work'. In 1850 William Pritchard of Caernarfon was granted a lease and he quickly developed the workings. A new quarry face was opened to the west of the public road in 1863 and a 100 yd long tunnel was cut under the road to link the old and new workings. Near to the tunnel entrance were the cutting and dressing sheds, the necessary machinery being driven by a water-wheel. The tunnel, leat, storage ponds and wheel pit can still be traced.

William Pritchard died in 1882 and his widow kept the business going for a while, but in 1890 it was said to have been 'quite recently abandoned, much to the sorrow of the neighbourhood as they afforded employment for a large number of men'. The quarry was reopened in 1894 by the Trevelyans of Nettlecombe Court, and 1,000 tons of slate were produced in 1904 and 1905. Existing price lists show products included roofing slates, chimney tops, hearth and headstones, staddle-stones, steps, window-sills, shelving and cisterns, but the quarry was rarely profitable and it closed again in 1910.

The final phase was from 1914 to 1938 when the Vickery family from Roadwater worked the quarry on a modest basis. After the Second World War the massive spoil heaps and suitable slopes were planted with conifers, but some of the old woodland survives and today there is a mile-long nature trail managed by the Exmoor Natural History Society. Follow yellow waymarks from track entrance off the Roadwater–Treborough road. This was opened in June 1982 and it is possible to walk the trail at any time and view the industrial remains together with the wealth of wildlife which is gradually recolonizing the old tramways, leat and spoil heaps.

Cleeve Abbey (GR ST047407)

The remains of the abbey lie north of the Brendon Hills, alongside the Washford River. Their importance today is due to the completeness of the living and sleeping quarters of the monks, and the other domestic buildings needed for the running of their Cistercian abbey. It was founded around 1188 by William de Romara, grandson of a Norman Earl of Lincoln, who made over all his lands at Cleeve in Somerset to Abbot Hugh of Revesby in Lincolnshire for the purpose of founding a new monastery. By 1198 the new site was colonized by twelve monks from Revesby under their first abbot, Ralph. Other gifts from local families added lands

Cleeve Abbey gatehouse.
(Drawing by Jonathan White.)

at Hungerford, Roadwater, Chidgley, Pit, Leigh and the Brendon Hills. The abbey was named *Vallis Florida*, the Valley of Flowers, although generally was referred to as Cleeve Abbey.

There is an interesting record of a man seeking sanctuary when Nicholas of Taunton fled to Cleeve Abbey in March 1317. He confessed to having stolen two maplewood cups valued at 9*s* and a tunic worth 3*s*. Ralph fitz Urse, coroner from Williton with a jury of twelve free men declared him guilty and an outlaw. He was allowed two days to leave the country by the port of Lyme Regis. The right of sanctuary in all monasteries, cathedrals and in some of the larger churches was increasingly abused by petty thieves and debtors in the Middle Ages. In 1624 James I cancelled and forbad all sanctuary rights in the country and so brought to an end a 500 years old custom.

The Cistercian Order, often called the White Monks from their white dress in contrast to the black habits of the Benedictines, were a working order mainly concerned with agriculture. They had generally strict ideals allowing no paintings, carvings, stained glass or ornament in their churches, but here at Cleeve seem to have deviated somewhat from the rules. There are still remains of vaulted ceilings, and painted decorations on plasterwork in the sacristy, chapter house and in particular a room known as the 'Painted Chamber' which may have been reserved as the abbot's personal office or a place for receiving guests. One painting depicts a bridge spanning a river with a variety of swimming fish.

The buildings are mainly of two dates. The east range with its fine dorter (dormitory) above the chapter house, sacristy and library is mainly of the thirteenth century, while the refectory over the kitchens and various chambers was remodelled at the end of the fifteenth century. Part of the cloister and the upper storey of the splendid gatehouse were rebuilt by the last abbot, Duvall, in the sixteenth century. A Latin inscription on the gatehouse can be translated 'Gate be open, shut to no honest person.' There is a fine tiled pavement remaining from the thirteenth-century refectory, each tile bearing various heraldic devices.

W.G. Maton, a geologist, passed along the Somerset coast in 1794 and called in to see the ruins of Cleeve Abbey. He writes that the 'site of the church is at present occupied by a shed for horses and cows. To the south stands the refectory, which may even now be called a noble room, though it is converted into a granary. It has a fine oak roof, adorned with various kinds of figures and emblems. The abbot's apartments occupied the eastern side and opposite to them, on the west, were the cells of the monks, now become stables to the adjoining farmhouse.' In 1875 the manor of Old Cleeve, which included the ruined abbey, was purchased by Mr G.F. Luttrell of Dunster Castle, who ended the farming use of the buildings and started the work of preservation.

Little remains of the abbey church except for the foundations on the north side of the cloisters. It was destroyed after the Dissolution but excavations in 1875–6 and 1931 revealed the plan of colonnaded nave, quire, presbytery and chapels and, despite its lack of walls, it remains today a site of peace and reflection. It is now in the care of English Heritage and there is a car park opposite the entrance.

Papermaking

For the past 200 years and more, papermaking has been an important industry in the Brendon Hills region especially at Watchet, and more recently at Pitt Mill (GR ST036365) by the old mineral line and close to the foot of The Incline. According to A.L. Wedlake in his *History of Watchet*, the manufacture of paper was carried out, from the Middle Ages onwards, by local farmers who would have found it a useful source of income during the winter. There is some evidence that the Watchet Mill originated in this way and was operated by the tenant farmer at Snailholt Farm between the present mill and the railway line. The mill appears to have been founded about 1750 by William Wood, who probably made coarse paper and strawboard, and it remained in the Wood family until it was taken over in 1846 by John Wansborough, William Peach and James Date. It continues to be known as the Wansborough Paper Mill although it is now owned by the St Regis Paper Co. Ltd.

Over the years it has provided employment for hundreds of local people, despite a great fire in 1898. A variety of fine papers were made and at one time there were converting departments where the huge reels of paper from the mill were cut into sheets. There was also a printing section. After the coming of the Great Western Railway, siding lines were run into the mill and also out on to the harbour so that trucks, loaded with esparto grass from Africa, used for the finest papers, could be filled straight from the ships' holds and run into the mill. Paper pulp from Scandinavian countries was also brought by sea.

The Washford River provided the mill with water and at one time there was little thought of pollution, for in the 1950s one never knew what colour the final reaches of the river would run when it emerged from the mill. It changed according to the colour of dye being used

Tim Patterson, Pit Mill Paperworks. (Photograph by Chris Chapman.)

in the paper manufactured – blue or green were quite attractive but reddish shades less so, especially when it reached the sea and flooded out into the Bristol Channel. Nowadays, the main production seems to be recycled papers and the piles of collected salvage stacked around the mill lack the romance of the former African and Scandinavian shiploads.

A complete contrast may be found on the higher reaches of the Washford River, bringing to mind those original farmer paper makers. At Pitt Mill may be found the Two Rivers Paper Company. This is run by Jim and Lynne Patterson who bought and restored the old water-mill in 1988. Their methods of manufacture must resemble those used by the early farmers. They produce handmade artists water-colour paper and each sheet is literally hand made in wooden moulds and after several processes is set to dry for about ten days in the loft of the mill. Most of the paper made is sold in the UK but about 15 per cent is exported. There is no pollution here as the water used comes from a well and is re-circulated.

Clatworthy and Wimbleball reservoirs (GR ST041311 and GR SS978316)

Water from the Brendon Hills impounded in these two reservoirs is a vital resource for the homes and many businesses in Somerset and Devon.

The River Tone which flows through and gives the county town of Taunton its name, rises on the Brendons near Burrow Farm in a swampy area known as Beverton Pond. About 2 miles south-east of its source the infant river flows into Clatworthy Reservoir, constructed by the former Taunton Corporation and opened on 6 July 1961 by HRH Princess Alexandra. It supplies water to Hinkley Point, Taunton and Wellington. When full the reservoir has a surface area of 130 acres and contains 1,180 million gallons of water. It has a 1½ mile nature trail running through Clatworthy Wood to the north of the dam. This skirts the defences of an Iron Age fort and is an interesting woodland walk with good views across the reservoir.

Wimbleball Lake near Brompton Regis is on a much larger scale. This was created as a joint project by South-west and Wessex Water Authorities. Work began in 1974, Wimbleball having been selected as the most suitable of seventeen sites considered. The first water was impounded in 1977 and extraction started during the dry spring of 1978 even before the reservoir was adequately filled up. A concrete dam spans the River Haddeo, a tributary of the River Exe. The Pulham River and other smaller waters also drain into the reservoir which, when full, holds 4,500 million gallons of water with a surface area of 374 acres. Water is taken from Wimbleball to the Taunton, Yeovil and Bridgwater areas via the Maunsdown treatment works and it can also be released to augment flow of the River Exe enabling extraction at Tiverton and Exeter in Devon.

At the northern end of the lake is Hurscombe Nature Reserve, managed by the Somerset Wildlife Trust. This is a good place to view wildfowl, especially in winter. Little grebe, great-crested grebe, cormorant, grey heron, Canada goose, widgeon (sometimes up to 250), teal, mallard, shoveler, pochard, tufted duck, goldeneye, goosander, coot, moorhen and common sandpiper are all regularly seen and, occasionally, osprey, Brent goose, ringed plover, green sandpiper and reed bunting.

Some unusual plants have been found in recent years near the water's edge, particularly when the level is low as it was in the summer of 1989, leaving an area of mud bank exposed. Golden dock (*Rumex maritimus*), shoreweed (*Littorella uniflora*), many-seeded goosefoot (*Chenopodium polyspermum*), creeping yellowcress (*Rorippa sylvestris*), water-purslane (*Lythrum portula*), water-pepper (*Polygonum hydropiper*), persicaria or redshank (*Polygonum persicaria*), and marsh cudweed (*Gnaphalium uliginosum*) all occur. Lady's-mantle (*Alchemilla xanthochlora*) grows by the nature trail and there are plenty of bluebells (*Hyacinthoides non-scripta*) in the woods at the southern end of the lake.

The full perimeter walk of the lakeside is about 12 miles and there are facilities for sailing. Picnic areas are provided and the lake is well stocked with rainbow trout. Fishing is restricted to traditional fly-fishing from the shore or a rowing-boat. Tackle is available for hire from the warden if required. The lake is a perfect place to spend a day out. A lecture room is also available at Hill Farm which may be hired by groups.

Two hundred years ago the Brendon Hill commons were enclosed to help improve the efficiency and output of agriculture. This meant more grass fields and hedgerows with sheep, cattle and milking cows. For a brief period it seemed that iron mining might engulf the hills, but the threat passed, and the scene today is largely a farming one. It is also a rather secret one, for visitors are few and the footpaths largely untrodden. For those who do come there is much to surprise and delight amid the Brendon Hills.

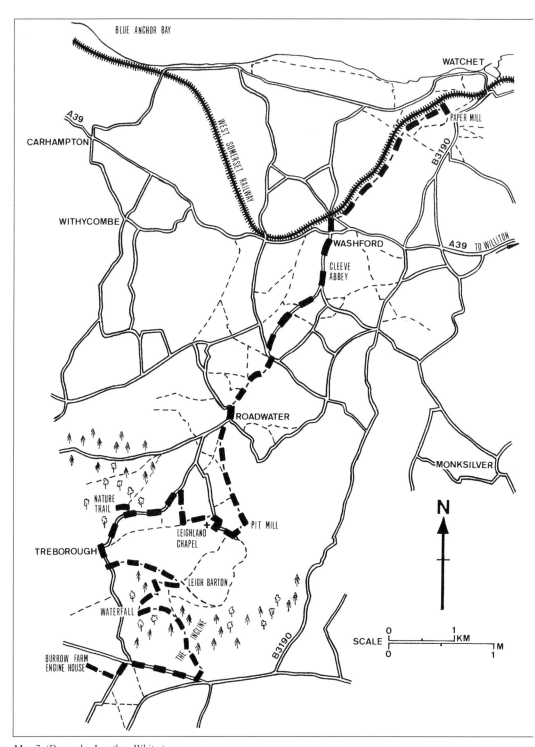

Map 7. (Drawn by Jonathan White.)

Burrow Farm to Watchet

Burrow Farm Engine House, Naked Boy Stone, The Incline, Forehill Wood and waterfall, Broadfield Wood, Leigh Barton Farm, Treborough Quarry, Leighland Chapel, Pitt Mill, Roadwater, Cleeve Abbey, Washford, Watchet. Distance: about 11½ miles. Maps: ST 03/13 and 04/14.

    This walk starts on the Brendon Hills at over 1,300 ft and descends to sea level at the port of Watchet. When you speed along the ridge road over these hills you can be forgiven for thinking that the landscape lacks interest. Today the area mainly consists of isolated farms but it has not always been so. In the mid-nineteenth century iron ore was mined here on a grand scale. With the associated workings were engine houses, miners' cottages, church and chapels, a school and a remarkable railway that took the ore down to the port of Watchet.

> **Park near Naked Boy Bridge (GR ST014344). Follow the signpost to Burrow Farm Engine House.**

    This is the sole surviving engine house on the Brendon Hills and is similar in design to the ones found in Cornwall. Built in about 1880, it housed a beam engine and was used to pump water from the mine and also to lift the ore.

> **Walk back along the bed of the railway, cross Naked Boy Bridge, visit the stone and then turn right along the B3224 until you pass the remains of the railway bridge at the top of The Incline. Just after Sea View House there is a public right of way. Turn left and follow the track down across The Incline and into Forehill Wood.**

    There are often clues to antiquities in a name. Burrow Farm is a corruption of barrow and is not to be confused with rabbits! Naked

Boy Stone is probably a Bronze Age standing stone, associated with the numerous barrows along the ridge. Local legend has it that a group of boys found with playing cards on a Sunday were changed into stone! Its more recent use is as a boundary stone between the parishes of Brompton Regis and Old Cleeve.

As the lane meets the road Sminhays Cottages are on your left. These are the only surviving miners' cottages in the Brendon Hill Village. At one time the village boasted a population of some 250 people.

Passing the remains of the railway bridge you will notice the ruins of a building on your left. We are now at the top of The Incline and this building housed the winding drums for pulling up the trucks from the bottom of the hill.

The building on your right is now a farmhouse but was once a temperance hotel and later a shop known as Davis's Stores. In the private grounds The Incline station still stands.

The Incline itself is overgrown with trees but you get a good view down it where the path crosses over. Completed in 1861, it has a gradient of 1 in 4, and is ¾ mile long. At its busiest time in the mid-1870s it carried 40,000 tons of ore each year and 19,000 passengers.

Just before you reach the waterfall in Forehill Wood you may notice, on your right, two large rusting drums which were once used for charcoal burning.

The waterfall is a miniature paradise, festooned in mosses and ferns. Trust the water and help yourself to a free shower!

Follow the track through the woods up to Leigh Barton and then take the path west until you reach the road. Turn right and walk down to Treborough Woods Nature Trail set in the old slate quarries.

The way to the nature trail is signposted down the private access road on the left. The trail is a mile long and well worth exploring.

These slate quarries date back to at least the fifteenth century but were worked on a large scale in the mid-1800s. As well as roof tiles they produced steps, window-sills, gravestones, cisterns and troughs (one can be seen against the building on your left at the main entrance. Note the way it has been bolted together.)

A new quarry face was started to the west in 1863, and in order to link the workings they cut a tunnel under the road. This is now blocked off at one end and gated at the other, making a perfect undisturbed home for the bat! The quarries ceased working in 1938.

> Continue down the road for half a mile and follow the sign to Leighland on your right. When you reach the chapel take the path down to Pitt Mill.

Unfortunately the old chapel of Leighland was completely demolished and rebuilt in 1862 and it lacks the charm of its predecessor.

As you reach the valley bottom you will see Pitt Mill on your left. This was originally a corn mill but now houses a small industry producing handmade paper for artists.

You are now back on the path of the old mineral line which runs down to Roadwater. The lane is straight here and is built on the bed of the line. As the road swings to the right note the rotting remains of two large old gates, one in the hedge and one in a private garden. These were positioned on the level crossing when the line was in use.

At one time the village of Roadwater had a number of industries including a blade mill for the making and grinding of edge tools, and a chandlery for making candles. Today a new industry, known as the Singer Instrument Co. makes high tech instruments for scientific research.

> Follow the road down to Cleeve Abbey.

The Cistercian abbey was founded in 1189 and had a farming community with the motto 'To labour is to pray'! Along with other smaller monasteries it was suppressed by Henry VIII in 1537. The abbey church was completely destroyed but what makes this site unique is the survival of the domestic quarters of the monks including a superb refectory and dormitory.

> Cross the A39 at Washford and cross the village playing field. You will then rejoin the bed of the old mineral line which now runs parallel to the West Somerset Railway down to Watchet.

Medieval tiled floor, Cleeve Abbey. (Photograph by Chris Chapman.)

The West Somerset line from Bishop's Lydeard to Minehead runs a regular service of steam trains. If you are lucky you may time the walk with the glimpse of a train.

WALK 6

At the next crossing which is a farm track, turn right through Kentsford Farm and follow the path past St Decuman's Well below the parish church.

Kentsford farm was originally the manor-house for Watchet with a history going back to the thirteenth century. Once you have walked through the fields the path joins a track up to the church. About halfway up on your left-hand side is the holy well of St Decuman. He was one of a number of Celtic missionary saints who brought the Christian gospel to the West Country in the sixth century.

At the beginning of the walk the ruins of the decaying industry up on the Brendon Hills had a romantic air about them, but in contrast, as you walk past the Watchet Paper Mill, the acrid smell is a sound reminder that the countryside is not always a green and pleasant land.

In Watchet you may wish to visit the museum which has a fine display of photographs and a model of the mineral railway.

Select Bibliography

Place of publication is given only if outside London

Clark, Evelyn V., *Walter Raymond, The Man, His Work and Letters*, J.M. Dent & Sons Ltd, 1933

Coleridge, Samuel Taylor, *Biographia Literaria*, eds. James Engell & W. Jackson Bate, 2 vols, 1983

——, *The Poems of Samuel Taylor Coleridge*, ed. Ernest Hartley Coleridge, Oxford University Press, 1912

Collinson, Revd John, *The History and Antiquities of the County of Somerset*, printed by R. Cruttwell, Bath, 1791

Dunning, Robert, *Somerset and Avon*, Edinburgh, John Bartholomew & Son, 1980

Hamilton, John & Lawrence, J.F., *Men and Mining on the Quantocks*, Bracknell, Town & Country Press, 1970

Hazlitt, William, *Essays. My first acquaintance with poets*, Blackie & Son, n.d.

Holland, W., *Paupers and Pig Killers, the Diary of William Holland, a Somerset Parson, 1799-1818*, ed. Jack Ayres, Stroud, Alan Sutton Publishing, 1984

Knight, Professor William, *Coleridge and Wordsworth in the West Country*, Elkin Matthews, 1913

Lawrence, Berta, *Quantock Country*, Westaway, 1952

——, *Coleridge and Wordsworth in Somerset*, Newton Abbot, David & Charles, 1970

Mayberry, Tom, *Coleridge and Wordsworth in the West Country*, Stroud, Alan Sutton Publishing, 1992

Nichols, Revd William Luke, *The Quantocks and Their Associations*, Sampson Low, 1891

Page, John Lloyd Warden, *An Exploration of Exmoor and the Hill Country of West Somerset*, Seeley, 1890

Pevsner, Nikolaus, *The Buildings of South and West Somerset*, Harmondsworth, Penguin Books, 1958

Sandford, Mrs Henry, *Thomas Poole and his Friends*, 2 vols, Macmillan, 1888

Sellick, Roger J., *The West Somerset Mineral Railway & the Story of the Brendon Hills Iron Mines*, Newton Abbot, David & Charles, 1962

Smith, Edward H., *Quantock Life and Rambles*, Taunton, Barnicotts, 1939

Waite, Vincent, *Portrait of the Quantocks*, Robert Hale, 1969

Wordsworth, Dorothy, *The Journals of Dorothy Wordsworth*, 2 vols, ed. and pub. William Knight, 1897

Wordsworth, William, *The Poetical Works of William Wordsworth*, ed. Thomas Hutchinson, Oxford University Press, 1917

Index